"You Have a Lot to Learn about Being a Wife."

He lowered his head, feathering his lips over the side of her neck. She arched her body as he moved to the curve of her chin and sought the corner of her mouth. Instinctively she shifted in his arms until their lips were fully mated. At first, his kiss was gentle, his lips barely touching hers as they softly grazed and teased; then it became more demanding as his tongue parted her lips and sought the company of hers. She felt herself drowning, caught in a vortex of passion she was still afraid to enter, but powerless to resist. . . .

JOANNA SCOTT

is a former teacher who gave up that career to follow her dream: writing. She has traveled widely, researching her novels, but is especially fond of California, the state that she and her husband of twenty-three years call home.

Dear Reader:

I'd like to take this opportunity to thank you for all your support and encouragement of Silhouette Romances.

Many of you write in regularly, telling us what you like best about Silhouette, which authors are your favorites. This is a tremendous help to us as we strive to publish the best contemporary romances possible.

All the romances from Silhouette Books are for you, so enjoy this book and the many stories to come. I hope you'll continue to share your thoughts with us, and invite you to write to us at the address below:

Karen Solem
Editor-in-Chief
Silhouette Books
P.O. Box 769
New York, N.Y. 10019

JOANNA SCOTT
Lover Come Back

Silhouette *Romance*

Published by Silhouette Books New York

America's Publisher of Contemporary Romance

Other Silhouette Books by Joanna Scott

Dusky Rose
The Marriage Bargain
Manhattan Masquerade
A Flight of Swallows

SILHOUETTE BOOKS, a Simon & Schuster Division of
GULF & WESTERN CORPORATION
1230 Avenue of the Americas, New York, N.Y. 10020

Copyright © 1982 by Joanna Scott

Distributed by Pocket Books

ISBN: 0-671-57169-9

First Silhouette Books printing August, 1982

10 9 8 7 6 5 4 3 2 1

Map by Tony Ferrara

America's Publisher of Contemporary Romance

Printed in the U.S.A.

Lover Come Back

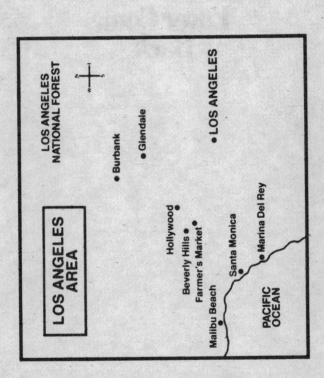

Chapter One

The white Mercedes exited the San Diego Freeway at Laguna Canyon and started cruising down the narrow two-lane road. It was early evening and the hot California sun had just melted into a rosy horizon. Palm trees swayed as a gentle breeze drifted in from the sea, cooling the beachfront community.

Jason Reynolds stubbed out his cigarette when he saw the *Hazardous: Fire Area* sign in the brush at the side of the road. Southern California was a naturally arid region, and devastating fires were an ever-present danger in its heavily wooded canyon areas. He glanced briefly at the chaparral-covered hills, studded with attractive, custom-designed homes perched on concrete-based stilts to expand the building sites and provide panoramic views of the countryside. Then his hands tightened on the wheel as his eyes returned to the winding road. He wasn't here to admire the scenery.

The sleek Mercedes snaked through the canyon until the road straightened into the main street of Laguna Beach. Jason's lips curled in a sardonic smile as he passed the Irvine Bowl Theater, site of the famed Festival of the Arts and Pageant of the Masters, then he turned left and drove along the crowded Pacific Coast Highway. The boardwalk to his right swarmed with departing sunbathers and locals just out for an evening stroll. Whitecaps foamed toward the shore and seagulls glided overhead, swooping down to snatch tasty tidbits left by careless picnickers. Disregarding these sights, Jason concentrated on the small shops and restaurants lining the opposite side of the street. Finally he found what he wanted and pulled the car into the gravel parking lot of a small coffeehouse.

After locking the car he entered the restaurant and was shown to a candlelit table at the far side of the room. His neatly styled black hair and hand-tailored dark gray suit stood out amid the long hair and tattered jeans of the other patrons, but this didn't seem to bother him and, looking perfectly at ease, he leaned back in his chair and ordered a cup of *cappucino*.

The noisy coffeehouse chatter subsided, and Jason's eyes shifted to the willowy girl who had just walked out onto the small stage at the front of the room. His bronze skin tautened over his aquiline features as he leaned forward in his seat to study her surreptitiously.

She carried her guitar to the edge of the stage and sat down, flinging her waist-length blonde hair over her shoulders and curling her long, slender legs beneath her. The plaintive rhythm-and-blues songs she strummed on her guitar set a musical mood, and she sang the accompanying lyrics in a clear, perfectly pitched voice. After she finished her set patrons put money into a small ceramic cup at the side of the stage. Then she walked through the restaurant carrying the cup and chatting with the diners. Several people slipped folded bills into her hand, and she smiled and thanked them.

Jason watched her thread through the darkness and moved his chair farther into the corner until not even the faintest glimmer of candlelight illuminated his hawklike face. The singer's head tilted doubtfully before she approached his table, then she shrugged and walked hesitantly toward him.

"Hello, I'm Linda Brown, the guitarist. I don't think I've seen you here before." Her blue eyes narrowed, seeking to discern the masculine features hiding from the flickering candlelight. "I hope you enjoyed the music." She smiled and held out a welcoming hand.

Jason's mouth twisted in a cruel, humorless smile. Grabbing her hand, he drew her to him, catching her easily between his spread legs. Her eyes blazed with anger as she tried to free herself, but he only increased the pressure and forced her onto his knee. As the space separating them vanished, her flashing eyes met his, then searched his face furiously. She gasped and caught her breath, her rage replaced by naked fear.

"You! What are you doing here?" Her voice was an uneven whisper.

His eyes devoured her features arrogantly. "I might ask you the same question, might I not?"

Linda's body grew taut as fear and anger battled within her. "I work here. . . . That's what I'm doing here. But it's hardly the sort of place I'd expect to find you."

Jason's dark eyes swept over her. "Quite right, my dear. This isn't my usual choice for an evening out. I'm only here to see you."

She twisted her hand in another unsuccessful attempt to free herself. "Let me go. I don't want to see you; we have nothing to discuss." She managed to stand up, but his legs were an unyielding vise, rendering her efforts to escape further an exercise in futility.

His free hand tilted her chin toward him so she could see his lips curl in an arrogant sneer. "On the contrary, we have quite a bit to discuss, although this isn't the place." He stood, curved his arm over her shoulders, and drew her protesting body against the lean hardness of his. "Let's get out of here."

She shook her head and struggled against him. "No, I have a ten o'clock show. I can't leave."

Lowering his head, Jason whispered ominously in her ear. "Tell them you don't feel well, tell them anything you want, but tell them you're leaving—unless you want a scene."

"All right. Just let me go. I'll meet you outside."

"No way. I'll be waiting right here, and don't try anything funny, because I'll only find you again."

Linda walked back to the stage, whispered a few words to the owner of the coffeehouse, picked up her guitar and returned to Jason. Wordlessly, he cupped her elbow and guided her to the door. Once they reached the parking lot he walked to the Mercedes and helped her inside. Then he settled himself behind the wheel and turned to her.

"I could take you to my place, but your home would be much more convenient since it's right in the area, and my home, as you know, is more than an hour's drive away. Will you give me directions?"

Linda shook her head. "There's no need for that. We can talk in the car."

"I haven't held a meaningful discussion with a woman in my car since I was a teenager." Jason laughed. "And you can well imagine how those conversations ended." A small, cynical smile curved his lips. "No, we'd better go to your house—unless you'd rather go to mine?" His tone made the words into a question.

She knew enough about Jason to realize that it was futile to argue; he always insisted on having his own way. "All right, Jason; I'm too tired to fight. Let's go to my house and get this over with."

Jason smiled triumphantly and drove from the parking lot, following the route Linda gave him. He stared straight ahead when they left the center of town and entered a dimly lit area where small, weatherbeaten cottages hung back from brown, weedy lawns. "You're thin, Linda . . . pale and tired-looking. Haven't you been well? If not for those big blue eyes, I wouldn't have known you."

"I'm just fine," Linda said. "And if I'd known that you would recognize me by my eyes, I'd have worn dark glasses."

Jason shifted his gaze to her. "My, my, what a nasty tongue you've developed, quite different from the innocent young thing you were when we first met. I wonder what can have turned you so bitter?"

"You of all people should know what destroyed my innocence and made me bitter."

Jason's lips lifted in an arrogant smile. "You're right about your innocence, but that doesn't explain your appearance or your attitude." He slowed the car as he approached an intersection. "Is this where I turn?"

Linda nodded. "Third house on the left," she said, pointing to a pink stucco cottage.

Jason pulled up to the curb and turned off the motor. His disdainful eyes narrowed as he took in the neglected lawn and peeling paint, and a disgusted grimace curved his lips as he surveyed the property. Linda opened her car door and ran into the house, quickly snatching things from the living room and tossing them haphazardly into the bedroom. She had just closed the bedroom door and was standing with her back resting against it when Jason walked through the front door. He scanned the room, evaluating the torn sofa with the spring popping through its cushions, the clean but threadbare carpet, and the gaudy travel posters tacked up on the walls to cover the cracking plaster. Shaking his head in disbelief, he sat on a plain wooden chair which Linda had tried to perk up with a coat of bright red paint. Then he motioned her toward the sofa.

"Sit down. There's no sense in making this more uncomfortable than it has to be."

"I'm fine. Just say your piece and get out. It's been a long day, and I'm tired."

Concern replaced the arrogance in Jason's dark eyes. "That's all the more reason why you should sit down."

Weakness drifted through Linda's body and, leaning against the wall, she edged her way to the sofa. Jason rose to help her, then sat down beside her. His fingers encircled her upper arms as he held her close to him.

"Now, are you ready to tell me what's been going on?" he asked.

Linda clenched her hands so tightly that her nails bit into her palms. "Why won't you believe that I have nothing to say to you? I'm just woozy because I haven't eaten. I usually have a sandwich between performances, but since you insisted I leave with you, I missed my dinner."

"I'm sorry," Jason said. "You should have told me; I'd have stopped at a restaurant." His hand shifted and he stroked the side of her neck. "Why don't you get yourself something in the kitchen? We can talk while you eat."

Linda shook her head. "There's nothing there. I was planning to shop tomorrow."

"I could run out and get something, but since we're leaving right away, I don't see any sense to that."

Linda pulled away. "What are you talking about? Leaving? I'm not going anywhere. . . . I live here."

Jason shrugged. "Everyone to his own taste. You can stay if

you like, but you have something of mine that's going home with me. That much I'm determined on. Whether or not you choose to come along is entirely up to you." He rose from the sofa and stood glowering down at her. "Very well, where is he?"

Linda's already pale complexion turned to chalk. "Where is who? I don't know what you're talking about."

Jason paced the length of the room. "Stop it, Linda. This farce has gone far enough. You look as if you're going to faint any second, and I find this hovel extremely depressing. The sooner we leave, the better. Where's the baby?"

"What baby? I don't know what you're talking about." She couldn't control the trembling that quivered through her body.

Jason halted directly in front of her, placing his hands on his hips and looking down at her pale face. "On the contrary, I think you know exactly what I'm talking about. My son, that's what I'm talking about. *Now* do we understand each other?"

Linda bit her bottom lip and tried to remain calm. "You're not making any sense at all. What could I possibly have to do with your son?"

Jason's mouth curved in a callous sneer. "Quite a bit, I'd say, since you happen to be his mother."

"No, it's not true."

"Cut it out, Linda. You're only wasting time. There's no point in denying what we both know for a fact."

Linda covered her face with her hands to hide the tears welling in her eyes. Her muted voice was punctuated by sobs. "How did you find out? I never wanted you to know."

"That's obvious, or I would have known long before this, wouldn't I? As it is, it took over a year of expensive detective work to find you, and I probably never would have succeeded even then if the detective hadn't spotted that old newspaper photo from the Pageant of the Masters. An amusing idea, having live models pose as works of art. You made a charming Madonna, and I suppose that was my son nestled so cozily in your arms . . . or was that only a doll? Was the baby too young to appear in the Pageant?" He tilted his head.

"Oh, well, it doesn't matter. You do have a son. The detectives discovered that and, knowing you, I have good reason to believe he's mine. That makes everything worthwhile, finding my son, I mean. Now, tell me where he is. I'm very anxious to see him."

"You can't have him. I won't let you. He's mine. There's no way I'll ever let you have him!" The impassioned words left her lips as a weak whisper.

"There's no way you can stop me. I'm taking him home with me tonight. I'd like you to come with us, but I can't force you."

"And you can't force me to give you my baby, either. You have no proof that you're his father. I'll deny everything."

"Really? And how old is he now? About nine months? The male offspring in my family tend to bear a strong resemblance to their father, and there's no reason to believe that my son would be any different. One quick glance should answer my question." He looked at her quizzically. "There's no need for that, is there? Your face has given me my answer."

"It doesn't matter. You have no claim to him. He means nothing to you—just another toy to satisfy your ego—but I love him; he's all I have. I cared for him when he was in my body and after he was born. All the pain and tenderness of birth and motherhood have been mine. You have no right to him."

Jason's fingers clamped over her shoulders. "So you think I have no right to him, that he means nothing to me. Well, you're wrong. Dead wrong. He happens to be the only child I have, and he's entitled to every luxury I can give him, but I've missed these parental pleasures because of your bitter vindictiveness. In order to deny me my son, you've deprived him of all the advantages that my wealth could give him."

"He doesn't need your money. I'm perfectly capable of caring for him."

"Are you really?" Jason sneered. "You don't even seem able to care for yourself, living in this dilapidated shack, faint with hunger and working in some sordid coffeehouse. Is that the life you're planning for my son? Well, forget it. I'll never allow it. I'm warning you, Linda, if you don't cooperate, there'll be a nasty custody battle, which you'll never win. You don't have the physical or financial strength to fight me, so you'd better stop this nonsense and start listening." He took a deep breath and captured her gaze with his. "Now, where is he? I want to take him home where he belongs."

Linda knew that everything Jason had said was true, and she knew he wouldn't hesitate to carry out his threats. He would take Andy, with her or without her, and she couldn't bear the thought of being parted from her baby. "He's with Mrs. Mason, the babysitter." Linda sighed. "I'll go get him."

"Wrong," Jason said. "You can barely stand on your feet; there's no way I'd trust you to carry a baby. I can't imagine what would have happened if the detective hadn't discovered your whereabouts yesterday and reported back to me this morning." He went into the bedroom and stuffed a few toys into a small tote bag Linda had left lying around. Then he asked her for Andy's medical records and added them to the toys. Finally he helped her off the sofa and held her against his side as they walked to the door.

She looked back hesitantly. "There are some things of mine I want to take."

He gripped her arm firmly. "Forget it. I'll get you whatever you need. Now, let's get out of here before you collapse."

She led Jason to a house midway down the street, then rang the bell and waited nervously for the door to be answered while Jason stepped back and out of sight. A rotund, gray-haired woman opened the door and looked at Linda with concern.

"Linda, you look terrible. I'm really worried about you. You should see a doctor. Why not leave Andy here tonight? He's sleeping so peacefully that it's a pity to disturb him. You can go to the doctor first thing in the morning, and I'll stay with Andy."

"That won't be necessary, Mrs. Mason. Linda's going to see a doctor tonight."

Mrs. Mason's eyes widened in shock when Jason spoke from the darkness. She looked at Linda for an explanation.

Linda was too tired and too weak to think up any convincing lies. "Mr. Reynolds is a friend of mine." Hmmph, she

thought, that was hardly an accurate description of Jason.
"He's invited Andy and me to stay with him for a while."

Mrs. Mason smiled. "I'm so glad to hear that. Linda's had
such a hard time managing. I don't know how much longer
she could have kept going without proper food just so the
baby would have everything he needed."

Jason's features were still hidden in the shrouded darkness
of the porch. "Linda and Andrew will be fine now. I promise
you, they'll be well cared for. Now, if you'll just give us the
baby, we'll be on our way. The sooner Linda gets to bed, the
better."

Mrs. Mason went back inside and Jason helped Linda off
the porch and into the car.

"You stay here," he said, tossing the tote bag into the back.
"I'll get Andrew."

"His name is Andy."

"Not on his birth certificate."

"Yes, but that's different. Andrew is so formal; I like to call
him Andy."

"Fine, but I intend to call him Andrew. That's his proper
name."

"And you're such a proper person, aren't you?"

"I try to be." He smiled smugly. "Now, shall we continue
this argument or shall I go in and get Andrew from Mrs.
Mason?"

"I owe her so much," Linda said. "She's been very good
about caring for Andy without being paid. She's never said
anything, but I know she's living on only her Social Security
checks. If you could give her some money I'll try to repay you
when I can."

"I'll take care of it," Jason said as he slammed the car door
and strode up the rickety porch steps to wait for Mrs. Mason
in the living room.

When she returned she was carrying a blue-blanketed
bundle and crooning to it softly. She looked up at Jason as she
prepared to hand him the baby. "Sakes alive, you're Andy's
father. He's the spitting image of you."

Jason smiled proudly. "Now you can understand why I'm
so determined to make things up to Linda and Andrew. This

is all the result of a terrible misunderstanding which I intend to correct immediately." He put his hand in his pocket. "You've been very kind to Linda and Andrew. There are some things money can't pay for, but I want you to have this. And no arguments." He took five crisp hundred-dollar bills from his wallet and put them in her apron pocket. "As soon as Linda feels better she'll be in touch with you."

He held out his arms, and Mrs. Mason handed him the baby. Gently, he pushed back the blanket and stared down at the infant, who was sleeping peacefully with his tiny fist curled against his cheek. Jason's smile broadened as he looked at Mrs. Mason. "He really does look exactly like me, doesn't he? How about that?" After kissing Mrs. Mason on the cheek, he took the baby to the car and placed him in the car bed behind the front seat. Then he started up the motor and headed for the freeway without a word to Linda.

Linda was exhausted, and both she and the baby were sleeping when Jason activated the electronically controlled gates leading to his Beverly Hills home. He drove onto its carefully manicured grounds where towering palm trees swayed above fragrant gardenias and massive brick planters of junipers and lantana bordered the dichondra lawn. In the center of the lawn a stone fountain misted the evening breezes with a cooling spray. Beyond sight of the road, at the end of the long, circular driveway and guarded by two closely planted rows of tall Italian cypress trees was a porticoed mansion whose broad stone steps opened onto a covered veranda. The white stucco exterior contrasted boldly with the red tile roof and lush greenery sprouting from colorful Mexican pottery attractively arranged on the terrazzo floor. The house looked every inch a Spanish hacienda.

Jason parked by the front steps, came around to Linda's side and gently removed the baby from the car bed he had bought just before driving down to Laguna. Linda stirred uneasily, but he patted her arm and closed the door softly. Then he walked up the steps and opened the front door. A young houseboy stepped into the brown-tiled entryway.

"Good evening, Kim. Is Miss Jenson still up?"

"Yes, Mr. Reynolds. We've all been waiting for you."

A tall, thin, middle-aged woman walked toward them. Jason eyed her impatiently. "Did you order the nursery furniture and baby supplies? Were they delivered?"

"Yes, Mr. Reynolds. Everything's been taken care of, and the small room in the wing opposite the master suite has been converted into a completely outfitted nursery. It wasn't easy getting delivery on such short notice, but I insisted; it didn't hurt to tell them money was no object."

Jason nodded and started up the stairs. "Did you call the domestic agency and arrange for a nurse for the baby?"

"Yes, that's all taken care of. She'll be here first thing in the morning."

"Very well," Jason said as he entered a bedroom stocked with baby furniture, toys and clothing. "In the meantime, ask Mrs. Smithers if she'll stay with the baby." He put Andy in the crib and tucked a blue thermal blanket around his chubby little body.

Miss Jenson was turning to leave when Jason's commanding voice caught her attention. "And Miss Jenson, get Dr. Stone on the phone. Tell him I want him over here immediately."

Miss Jenson raised her eyebrows. "But it's nearly midnight, Mr. Reynolds."

Jason turned from the crib and glared at his secretary. "I'm well aware of the time, Miss Jenson. I said I want Dr. Stone over here immediately; do I make myself clear?"

Miss Jenson's hauteur shriveled under his icy stare. "Yes, Mr. Reynolds. I'll take care of it right away." She left the room.

"Thank you," Jason said wryly, following her into the hall.

A small plump woman was coming up the circular stairway and Jason motioned toward the bedroom he had just left. "I know you've had a busy day, Mrs. Smithers, but I'd be most appreciative if you'd stay with the baby tonight. Miss Jenson has stocked all the necessary supplies. A baby nurse will be here in the morning, but in the meantime we could use your help."

"I understand, Mr. Reynolds, and don't you worry about a thing. I'm an old hand at caring for babies. I've raised five of my own, you know." She smiled and headed for the nursery.

Jason waited until she had closed the door, then he began walking down the stairs. He returned to the car and lifted Linda in his arms. She stirred restlessly and nestled her head against his chest, then her arms crept around his neck as she sought added support. Jason kicked the car door shut and walked into the house, carrying her upstairs and into a small bedroom adjoining the master suite. The blankets had already been turned back, and Jason set her down on the ecru satin sheets.

Miss Jenson rapped on the open door before walking in. "Dr. Stone will be over in ten minutes. He was quite annoyed when I couldn't explain the reason for his visit."

Jason was unperturbed. "I'll tell him when he gets here. He should know that I wouldn't bother him unnecessarily." He looked down at Linda, who had curled up and was still sleeping peacefully. "Do you have something she could wear? Those jeans don't look very comfortable for sleeping."

Miss Jenson thought for a minute. "She's thin, isn't she? My things would be too big, and no one else on the staff is even close to her size."

Jason made a wry face. "Well, I don't suppose there's anything we can do about it at this time of night. I was so concerned about the baby that I forgot about her. Make a note to order some clothing tomorrow, will you please? Call up one of those shops on Rodeo Drive and get whatever you think she needs. In the meantime, put her into one of my pajama tops. I'm going downstairs to wait for Dr. Stone."

Jason was seated in the library when Kim showed Dr. Stone into the room. He waited until Kim had left and shut the door before he began speaking. "Sit down, Ken. Can I get you a drink?"

Stone slammed his medical kit down on the desk. "Just a minute, Jason; you didn't get me out of bed in the middle of the night to join you in a late-night drinking session, did you?"

"I was just trying to be cordial, Ken. I haven't called you here on a whim. What I have to tell you is confidential and not easy for me to talk about. Your hostility isn't helping matters."

Jason's sober words had a calming effect on Ken, who was as much his friend as his doctor, and the other man settled himself into a big leather club chair beside the fireplace.

Jason rested his arm on the mantel, tossed back his drink and began to speak. "About a year and a half ago I met a young girl. I think she was nineteen at the time. The details of our relationship are unimportant right now. Suffice it to say that I've just found out that she has a nine-month-old child . . . my son. I've brought them here from Laguna Beach, where I found them living in a house that was no better than a shack. The baby looks fine, although I would like you to check him while you're here; however, his mother seems sick. She's much thinner than she was before, and she's pale and weak. She's upstairs sleeping now, and I don't know if it's from exhaustion or illness. I'd like you to have a look at her."

Stone's breath came out in a whistle. "Good Lord, Jason, you really know how to shock a man out of his sleep, don't you? I take it you're not married to the girl?" He watched while Jason shook his head. "Then I can't treat her. I need the consent of the patient or her next of kin."

Jason drained his glass and headed for the door, motioning for Dr. Stone to follow. "She has no next of kin; her parents died in a plane crash right before she came to L.A." He took a deep breath and grimaced. "I'll get you her consent."

He went up the stairway and into the room where Linda was sleeping. Gently, he shook her shoulders until she opened her eyes and glanced sleepily around her. In spite of her nap, she still seemed completely exhausted. She tried to turn away and close her eyes again, but Jason spoke insistently, demanding her attention. "Linda, this is Dr. Stone. He's going to examine you and try to make you feel better."

Linda shook her head. "I don't need a doctor. I feel fine. I'm just tired; I'll be okay once I get some sleep."

"Now listen, Linda." Jason's voice thundered with authority. "You're not well, and if you don't let Dr. Stone check you over we'll probably have to put you in a hospital, where you won't be able to see Andrew. You wouldn't like that, would you?" Linda shook her head, fear in her deep blue eyes. "Very well then, does Dr. Stone have permission to examine you?"

Linda nodded, and Jason walked to the window while Ken Stone started taking instruments from his medical bag. The examination was quite thorough, and when he was finished, Dr. Stone motioned for Jason to follow him out of the room. Linda turned over and went back to sleep, as if the events of the evening had left her too drained and confused to function. Jason and Ken Stone whispered in the hall.

"Well, how is she?" Jason asked.

"I can't be positive. It's difficult to do a complete examination in the house. If you want to be really sure, you can bring her to my office tomorrow and I'll run some tests. However, right now, I'd say she's suffering from a mild case of malnutrition and a slight touch of the flu. Some good food and bed rest should get her back on her feet. I can give her an antibiotic to help keep the flu under control, but the rest is going to take time."

Jason nodded. "That sounds fine. You give her the antibiotic and I'll see to the diet and bed rest."

After Dr. Stone had injected the antibiotic he followed Jason to the nursery, where Miss Jenson and Mrs. Smithers were still getting things in order. Jason thanked them and asked them to wait outside while the doctor checked the baby. Ken Stone looked at Andy and then back at Jason.

"There's not much doubt about the father, is there?"

Jason flashed a proud smile.

Stone look surprised. "And you don't seem very upset about it, either. Funny, I didn't have you pegged as the doting-father type."

Jason shrugged. "Just goes to show how little you know about your patients. I happen to like children, and I've become especially fond of my own son."

Stone lifted his eyebrows. "You're not just saying that because his mother is threatening you with a nasty paternity suit, are you?"

Jason shook his head. "On the contrary, I had to search to find her. She was very anxious to keep me from learning about the baby."

Ken Stone picked up his medical bag and snapped it shut. "Well, Jason, I've had about as many surprises as I can stand in one evening. Your son looks perfectly healthy to me. However, I'll give Miss Jenson the name of an excellent pediatrician and she can schedule an appointment. Keep in touch and let me know how Linda is getting on." He shook Jason's hand and went downstairs with Miss Jenson.

Jason turned to Mrs. Smithers. "Can you sleep here tonight? You can let your other duties slide for a while. We'll manage." He gestured toward the child. "Right now, he's more important than anything."

Mrs. Smithers nodded and returned to the nursery. Jason caught Miss Jenson as she stepped off the stairway. "Did Dr. Stone give you the information about the pediatrician?" he asked.

Miss Jenson nodded.

"Fine," Jason said. "We'll take care of that in the morning; let me know if there are any problems. We'd better get some sleep for now. We've all had quite a day." He went into the master suite, changed quickly, dropped onto the canopied, king-sized bed and was asleep almost immediately.

Chapter Two

The bright California sun blazed through the leaded-glass French doors leading from the balcony to Linda's bedroom. Her long lashes fluttered open, and she stretched languidly on the smooth, silk sheets. The sun's warmth stroked her skin like a lover's tender caress, and for the first time in months she enjoyed a blissful feeling of calm. She had almost forgotten what tranquility could be like.

Then as she came fully awake, her memory returned and she bolted up in bed. Jason's large blue silk pajama top slid from her shoulders and she retrieved it quickly, clutching it tightly around her neck in an attempt to shield her softly curving breasts. After a cursory survey of her surroundings she swung her legs off the bed and tried to stand. The sudden movement made her dizzy, and she fell against the night table. As she gripped the table for support, a small bisque lamp tipped, hitting the carpet with a muffled thud.

Instantly the connecting door flew open and Jason strode in. His thick, dark hair was still damp from a recent shower and the muscles of his bare chest rippled beneath his half-buttoned white silk shirt. His angry glare cut through her as he quickly covered the distance separating them. "Just where do you think you're going?" he asked, lifting her onto the bed and pressing her shoulders back against the pillows. "Don't you know you're too weak to be on your feet?" He crossed his arms over his chest, stepped back and stared down at her.

At first Linda shuddered and shrank away from his over-powering frame, then she bit her lower lip and forced herself to speak. "I was getting up. What did it look like I was doing? And my feet are perfectly fine, thank you." She sat up, pulled the sheet over her shoulders and shifted her body away from Jason.

He dropped to the side of the bed, blocking her. "Get back in bed. You're not going anywhere."

She drew the sheet closer to her neck. "Don't you tell me what to do, Jason Reynolds. I'm getting out of here and you can't stop me."

"You don't really believe that, do you?" Jason sneered. "I was going to give you a chance to rest before continuing our discussion, but now I don't think it can wait." He stood and began pacing the room. "I'm sorry about what happened between us, but surely you can see that you were as much to blame as I was."

Linda caught her breath and tightened her lips. *"I'm* to blame? How can you say that? I had just moved here from Kansas. . . . My parents had died. . . . I didn't know anyone. . . . I was lonely and I went to that party to meet some people. . . ."

"Well, you did. You met me."

"The way things turned out, I would have been better off staying home."

"Did you ever think that I might feel the same?"

"You? How? It wasn't your first Hollywood party. You weren't a gullible little hick."

"And you were?"

"You know I was . . . until I met you."

Jason came to a standstill in front of her. "All right, I'm not proud about what happened either. Despite what you think about my social life, I almost never attend those damned parties. I was just leaving the building after a business meeting when I glanced into the room and found myself looking straight into your big blue eyes. How was I supposed to know that you were some innocent virgin who thought she was attending a high school prom? Young, attractive starlets are invited to these studio parties for the sole purpose of entertaining the male guests. The rumors you've heard about the importance of the casting couch in many a young girl's show-business career aren't entirely false, you know."

"Well, you could have stopped when you found out I

wasn't like that. I didn't know about these parties. This girl at the hotel where I was staying invited me; we had just gotten there when you walked in." She was too ashamed to admit that she had thought he was the handsomest man she had ever seen. She would never let Jason know how strongly attracted to him she had been from the very first moment she had seen him. He would only laugh and make fun of her naïveté, and she had had her fill of that. "Then, when you told me you were the head of JMR Records and invited me to come to your home and audition for you, I went with you willingly." Her mouth curled in disgust. "Unfortunately, I had no idea what role you wanted me to audition for."

Jason turned and started to pace the room again. "All right, I admit we got our signals crossed. You gave me every reason to believe you were attracted to me, and by the time I realized that you weren't a willing partner things had gotten too far out of control for me to stop. But when I woke up in the morning and wanted to make things up to you, you were gone. I had detectives trying to find you for over a year, but they had no luck until they saw that picture and then spotted you at that tawdry cafe in Laguna Beach."

"There's nothing tawdry about it. It's a neighborhood coffeehouse, and the owner is a complete gentleman, which is more than I can say for you."

"Do you mean to say that you've been living a puritan existence in that wild artists' colony?"

Linda was seething. "Yes, you'd probably consider it that. Does it shock you so much to know that other men respect me as a person . . . that they don't see me as an object to be cajoled into letting herself be used?"

Jason flashed a mocking grin. "On the contrary, I'm rather pleased. It will make our marriage much easier . . . no disappointed lovers to deal with."

"What marriage? I haven't the slightest intention of marrying you. I despise you."

"That's too bad, because you don't have any choice. Most girls would have demanded money for an abortion or threatened me with a paternity suit, but you did neither. You went into hiding and had my son without ever telling me about him. Despite the low rating you put on my morality, I'm not in the habit of seducing innocent young virgins. Most of my lady friends are much too experienced to let something like this happen. Our son is my only heir, and he means a lot to me. I'm not going to subject him to painful taunts about his birth and lack of a father, so, even if you hate me, our marriage *will* take place and Andrew *will* grow up in my home, with all the luxuries and advantages my substantial wealth can provide. Now that I've found him, I won't let you keep him in that hovel in Laguna any longer. I mean to have him, Linda, and I won't let you stop me, but I'm willing to have you, too, because that would be best for Andrew. Am I making myself clear?"

Linda's body seemed to sag. She closed her eyes and leaned against the headboard. "I don't have much choice, do I? Not if I want to keep Andy." She had already learned that Jason never gave you a choice, and he didn't know the meaning of the word "compromise." What was the point of fighting him? He would never give up until he got his way, so she would only lose in the end, anyway. How had the newspapers described him? "Tenacious"—that was it—tenacious as a bulldog when he wanted something. She threw back her shoulders and her eyes met his. "All right, I may have to marry you for Andy's sake, but that's where my commitment ends. I do not intend this to be any more than a paper marriage. I'm not as simple as I used to be, and I won't be so helpless the next time you try one of your little seduction numbers."

"Don't flatter yourself," Jason replied. "I can easily survive without you. You don't attract me in the least. Have you looked in the mirror lately? Your face is drawn and haggard, your body thin and shapeless; if you had looked like this when I first saw you, we probably wouldn't have met. There'd be no Andrew, no reason for us to get married. So don't worry about any husbandly demands. I'll have no trouble satisfying my needs elsewhere. I never have." Turning, he left the room and slammed the door behind him.

Linda pressed her face into the pillow and wept hopelessly. Everything Jason had said about her and her inability to take

proper care of Andy was true. Only her stubborn pride had
kept her from asking for his help. If he hadn't found her
yesterday, she probably would have collapsed from hunger
and exhaustion, and then what would have happened to
Andy? He would have been placed in a foster home or
adopted by strangers, without ever knowing who his real
parents were. No, Jason was right; she couldn't deny Andy all
that he was offering. She'd suppress her own feelings about
Jason and marry him for Andy's sake. But, she thought,
ashamedly remembering her own passionate responses on the
night Andy was conceived, never would she allow herself to
be duped into thinking that Jason really cared about her. She
knew too much about him now ever to think that again.

Although she hadn't seen Jason during the past year and a
half, she had taken a perverse pleasure in searching the
newspapers and reading every article she could find about
him. It was an obsession with her, and the more she learned
about him, the more her hatred grew. She found that he was a
demanding businessman with an uncanny knack for knowing
exactly what the public wanted. His insight was so perfect that
JMR Records had expanded into films through JMR Productions and was now known as JMR Industries.

Oh, how she hated watching his business bloom while her
career withered on the vine. Although she loved Andy more
than life itself, she had always wanted to be a professional
singer, and she would never forgive Jason for destroying any
chance she might have had. She had been sure that she would
never see him again, and had been determined not to let him
know about Andy, yet now they were living in his home, and
she had agreed to marry him.

Her morbid musings were interrupted by a series of light
raps on the bedroom door, and before she could answer, Miss
Jenson had walked in, carrying a white wicker tray. Linda
raised herself against the back of the bed and waited while
Miss Jenson placed the tray in front of her. The older woman
removed the silver cover from the breakfast plate and Linda
stared down at a huge platter of bacon, eggs and fried
potatoes. She made a face, pushed it aside and reached for

the fresh melon, toast and coffee that sat to one side. "This will be fine. I never eat much for breakfast."

Miss Jenson looked at her as if she were a misbehaving child. "I'm sorry, Mrs. Reynolds, but Mr. Reynolds left orders for you to eat everything on the tray, and things go much more smoothly around here if we all do as he asks."

Linda hid her surprise at being addressed as Mrs. Reynolds. Either Jason had told his staff that they were already married or he didn't really intend to legalize their living arrangement. In any case, she felt that this wasn't the time to correct Miss Jenson. This was Jason's little game and, as he had so callously pointed out, she wasn't in any position to question the rules. She began eating and was amazed at how hungry she actually was. Miss Jenson brought a chair to the bedside and started making notes on a small pad she had pulled from one pocket.

"There are several things I need your help with, Mrs. Reynolds. I wonder if we could talk while you're having breakfast. I have so much to do, and this would save some time."

Linda stopped eating and nodded. "That's fine, Miss Jenson. I'll be happy to help any way I can."

"Thank you. First of all, the pediatrician would like a list of Andrew's inoculations. Do you have that information?"

Linda pointed to the carryall at the side of the room. "It's in there. Will you please hand it to me?" She took the tote bag, reached in and pulled out a small yellow card. "He received all his shots at the Orange County Medical Clinic."

Miss Jenson raised her eyebrow. "Well, from now on he'll be under the care of Dr. Joel Hardings, one of the finest pediatricians in Beverly Hills. He's not taking on any new patients, but Dr. Stone has spoken to him and he's agreed to see us." She smiled benignly at Linda. "Mr. Reynolds has also asked me to order some clothing for you, so if you'll tell me your sizes I'll arrange for enough to keep you going until you can get to the shops yourself."

Linda shook her head. Andy might benefit from Jason's money, but she would not. She wasn't going to let him add "gold digger" to the list of unattractive accusations he had flung at her. "I don't need any clothes. As soon as I feel better, I'll drive down to Laguna and pick up my own things."

Miss Jenson lowered her eyes to Jason's pajama top, which was falling off Linda's shoulders. "I think we'd better get you some clothing right away," she said meaningfully. "You'll make my job much easier if you'll just give me the information I need without arguing."

Linda's hand went to her neck and she pulled the edges of the shifting pajama top together. "I suppose you're right. I could use a few things right away; I'd better tell you my sizes."

Miss Jenson smiled. "That would make everything a lot simpler," she said, and began writing down the information Linda gave her. "Things are always so much easier when everyone cooperates," she said, giving Linda the impression that Jason's home was some sort of feudal kingdom where everyone bowed to the lord and master's will.

"You don't mean cooperate, you mean obey, don't you?" Linda asked.

"We like to think of it as a cooperative effort to keep Mr. Reynolds' affairs in order and his home running smoothly." The woman hesitated for a minute. "It's really none of my business, but I don't think it would be wise to do anything to upset him. He does like to have things his way," she said pointedly. She completed her notes, closed her book and rose to leave. "Mrs. Smithers will come for the tray when you're finished. I'll get on this right away. When the nurse arrives, I'll bring her in and you can tell her whatever she needs to know about Andrew."

Once she was alone again Linda tried to swing her feet off the bed and stand, but she felt so weak and dizzy that she had to lie back down almost immediately. Though her breakfast might have been healthy for her, it had made her stomach even queasier, and there wasn't much point in getting up until she was over these flu-like symptoms.

So Jason liked to have things his own way. Well, didn't everybody? The difference was that Jason usually got what he wanted. But not where she was concerned, not anymore.

Still, he had probably been right in one respect, she thought: rest—she needed rest, and plenty of it. Turning over on her side, she drifted back to sleep. The next thing she knew, her shoulders were being gently shaken. When she opened her eyes, she saw Jason standing beside the bed.

"I'm sorry to wake you, but some people are waiting to meet you. Do you think you can sit up and slip into this?" Sliding his hands beneath her arms, he lifted her until her back rested against the headboard.

Linda took the man's robe he handed her and shrugged her arms into it. The brown terrycloth was more concealing than what she was wearing, and she pulled it firmly across her breasts. "Well, I suppose this is a bit more circumspect than your pajama top, but it's hardly suited to entertaining. Who am I meeting?"

Jason tilted his head and studied her for a moment before speaking. "Ken Stone will be here—you met him last night— and his wife Cindy, and Judge Mallory. He's going to marry us; Ken and Cindy will be witnesses. My staff assumes that we're already married; I felt it would be in Andrew's best interest to tell them that we married last year while I was out of town and separated almost immediately, after a quarrel. In any case, the sooner we make our marriage a reality, the better I'll feel. I don't want to chance someone discovering that you're not really my wife."

Linda frowned. "Isn't it possible that they'll find out we've just been married. This kind of secret is hard to keep."

"I've thought about that. That's why I'm having Judge Mallory marry us confidentially. He's a good friend of mine, and he'll be as discreet as possible. The fact that he's a superior court judge who knows about the length of our relationship—and about Andrew—lets him issue the license without a blood test, so we can be married immediately. Ken and Cindy are aware of the delicacy of the situation, so they can be trusted to keep things under wraps. If, in spite of all our precautions, the truth does get out, at least we'll be married, and the gossip will be a lot less damaging than if we weren't. But that's simply a risk we'll have to take. Of course, all these problems could have been avoided if you had come to me when you first discovered your condition. Better yet, you should never have behaved like such an adolescent and run away in the first place."

"I *am* an adolescent. Don't you remember? You made my lack of sophistication quite clear when we first met. I was hardly a fit companion for a sophisticated man of thirty-five. Why should you have expected me to behave any different-ly?"

Jason looked at her derisively. "All right, have it your way. Just so you understand that I intend to do everything I can for my son. Don't fight me on that." He stalked out of the room.

When he returned, the Stones and Judge Mallory were with him. Jason made the proper introductions and the required amount of polite chatter took place, but an air of embarrassed discomfort shrouded the room, and finally Jason suggested that they proceed with the ceremony. From that point on, things moved quickly, and, almost before Linda could realize what was happening, Jason had slipped a plain gold ring on her finger. They were married. It was just that simple and just that cold. There were no sentimental words of endearment, no frilly white gown, no joyous relatives, not even a kiss between the bride and groom to seal the marriage with love.

Since the ceremony had been performed in accordance with Jason's instructions, it had been very businesslike, setting the tone for a marriage that would be a business arrangement calculated merely to provide the home and lifestyle Jason wanted for his son. Linda bit her lower lip and brushed a tear from her eye at the chilling vision of a loveless eternity stretching before her.

Jason caught her gesture and bent to whisper in her ear. "Come now, sweetheart, marrying me isn't as bad as all that; most women would jump at the chance to be Mrs. Jason Reynolds." Before Linda could answer he had straightened and walked away to shake Judge Mallory's hand and thank him. "And now I think we'd all better leave and let Linda get some rest." He started for the door, then hesitated, as if he'd had second thoughts. "Ken, why don't you give her a quick checkup? Just to see how the antibiotic's working. When you're finished, we'll be waiting in the library."

After the others had gone, Ken approached the bed. He looked at Linda, then opened his black bag and asked how she was feeling. When he had finished the examination and was putting back his instruments, he said, "Well, the antibiotic seems to have the flu under control and, after some of Mrs. Smithers' good cooking, you should be well on your way to recovery." He smiled and he walked to the door. "I'm very happy to have been here today. I didn't think I'd ever see Jason married; now he's a father to boot. You just rest up; you're a very lucky young lady."

When he had gone, Linda sighed and leaned back against the pillows. "Lucky" was hardly the word she would have used to characterize herself. During the past year, "stupid" had been the description she had used most often. How could she have been stupid enough to go to Jason's house when she knew nothing about him except that his sensuous gaze sent shivers racing up her spine, dangerous shivers that should have made her wary? She was anything but lucky. Meeting Jason Reynolds had been the low point of her life, although she hadn't known it at the time. He had been the most exciting man she had ever met; his low, soothing voice had intoxicated her, and she had only wanted to please him.

To please him . . . That had been her undoing, because she *had* pleased him—temporarily—until he discovered she was a virgin, and then . . . She closed her eyes, trying to block out the memory of Jason's angry tirade, all those accusations, those horrible names he had thrown at her. She had been too ashamed to face him and had run away as soon as he had fallen asleep. Yet once she had left him and given herself a chance to think about what had happened, she had realized that she was the one who should have been angry. He had lured her to his house with false promises. He had taken advantage of her naïveté, then blamed her for giving in to him. In that moment all her potential love for him had turned to hate. And she hated him still.

But Andy was hers. He was the one good thing that had

come out of her night with Jason, and no matter what Jason said, she wouldn't let him take Andy from her. She might have been a lovestruck girl when she first met Jason, but she was a woman now, a woman who would never forgive him for the way he had treated her. She sighed and forced herself to relax. Fighting with Jason would have to wait. Right now she was too exhausted to do anything, and a little while later, after eating the lunch Mrs. Smithers brought her, she went back to sleep.

The dusky skies of late afternoon were just beginning to darken the window when she woke, feeling so much better that she decided to get out of bed. Jason's pajama top came almost to her knees, yet it hung from her shoulders so loosely that it was almost useless as a covering. As for his robe, it was so long that she tripped over its hem if she took more than two steps. She couldn't keep wearing this outfit, so she began looking for her own clothing, but she couldn't find it anywhere.

She was restless and wanted to get out of this room, but there didn't seem to be much she could do until she got her hands on some clothes. It was hardly practical for her to wander through the halls looking for Andy while she was falling over her own feet. Still, she had to do something, she couldn't stay in bed all day. Glancing through the open bathroom door, she saw a large pink marble tub and decided to take a bath. A bath always refreshed her and helped her to think clearly, and a clear head was exactly what she needed when dealing with Jason. Never again would she let her wishful thinking turn him into the handsome prince of her girlhood dreams.

The water streamed from the faucet and Linda added some scented bubble bath from the marble counter. She watched it foam, then slipped off the robe and pajama top and stepped into the soothing warmth. She had closed her eyes and was relaxing, her head back against the tile, when her skin tingled with a heat that didn't come from the steamy water. She opened her eyes and saw Jason leaning against the doorjamb, his arms across his chest.

"What are you doing here?" she asked, sliding deeper into the water and trying to hide her flaming skin under the bubbles.

"I came to see how you were feeling. You shouldn't be out of bed yet, and certainly not in a bath, unattended. You could black out. Ken wants you to stay in bed for a few more days."

Linda stared back at him defiantly. "Well, I didn't black out and I feel just fine. Now, if you'll be good enough to leave, I'll get out."

Jason picked up a large terry bath sheet from the electrically heated towel rack and held it open over the tub. "Come on, hop out. I'll dry you off and help you back to bed."

Linda sank lower in the water. "That's not necessary. I can do it myself. You don't belong in here."

Jason smiled arrogantly. "It's my house."

"But this is my room, and I deserve some privacy in my bath, at least."

Jason shook his head. "You're my wife. . . . There are no secrets between us."

"I'm not really your wife. I only married you because of Andy. You know that as well as I do."

Jason reached down and, gripping her under the arms, lifted her out of the tub. Quickly, he wrapped her in the bath sheet and carried her into the bedroom. He sat down on the bed and held her in his lap, moving the towel in gentle, circular motions as he began to dry her body. Even with the thickness of the towel between them her skin prickled in response to his touch. He pulled the edges of the towel together, held them with one hand and combed the other through her hair. Her head tilted back, and his eyes commanded her attention as they slid over her face.

"Why you married me doesn't really matter. The point is that we are married. The ceremony and the piece of paper we signed make our marriage as valid as any in the state of California. I now have the same legal rights as any other husband, so don't try setting your own limits."

Linda's eyes widened and she tried to pull away from him. "But you promised. . . . You said that you wouldn't make any demands . . . that you found me unattractive."

Jason released the towel and slipped his hand behind her back, drawing her to him. "And you made some rather interesting promises yourself," he taunted, "to love, cherish, even to obey. Don't they count at all?"

"That was only a meaningless formality." She pressed her palms against his chest and tried to create some space between them, but Jason tightened his grasp, nullifying her efforts. She felt trapped and knew he was enjoying her helplessness against the superiority of his physical strength. "Why are you doing this?"

"Because I'm used to having my way, and I don't like dealing in ultimatums unless I'm deliveri.ig them. It's true that I don't find you particularly attractive at this moment, but as we've learned"—he smiled sardonically—"life has a way of surprising us, and I don't know how I'll feel in the future."

"But *I* do. *My* feelings aren't going to change." She might not have his physical strength, but she wasn't about to accept verbal defeat, as well.

"Well, that's too bad, isn't it? Because you really don't have much choice."

"That's not true. I have the same choices you do, and I don't like ultimatums, either. I was a fool to trust you. You can forget this ridiculous marriage idea. I'm leaving, and I'm taking Andy with me. We'll get a divorce, and as long as you know about him, I'll count on your child support payments to give him the sort of life you feel is so necessary."

Jason's hands moved under her arms and his thumbs traced the curve of her breasts. He paid no attention to her breathless gasp and continued to hold her tightly. "That's one choice you don't have," he said softly, "taking Andrew away from me. You can get a divorce if you like. My home isn't a prison, and I can't stop you from leaving, but Andrew stays."

"You know I'll never leave without him."

"Then you have no choice, do you?" His hands left her body and he reached for the fresh pajama top folded at the foot of the bed.

The towel fell to the floor as she slid off his lap and tried to get away from him. He caught her wrist, stopping her flight,

and she stood before him, completely exposed to his penetrating gaze.

"Let me go." Her free hand covered her body, trying to
shield it from the eyes that were eating into her flesh.

"I don't think so." His voice was husky. "Our marriage is
beginning to look better to me already." Drawing her body
against his, he stroked her back and caressed the gentle slope
of her hips. "I've never forgotten how you felt." His hand
teased her and she reddened with both shame and desire.

His touch was too much. It brought back memories Linda
had fought hard to forget, and unable to control the involuntary reaction of her body, she trembled beneath his fingers.
The stroking stopped, and his body grew rigid as he held her
away from him. As she remembered the past, she felt colder
and more alone than ever, but she tossed her head back and
kept her feelings hidden from Jason. Had he only been
interested in seeing her reaction? Was that why he had
stopped? Didn't he realize that no matter how much he
aroused her sensual responses, she'd never again let him use
her body merely to satisfy his own needs? Or would she? Her
skin was too taut and her breath too husky for her to be sure
of anything.

"I'm sorry," he said. "Seeing you like that . . . I forgot you
were sick." He slipped the pajama top over her shoulders and
lifted her onto the bed. "I won't argue with you. You can
have things your way for now." He pulled the covers over her
and adjusted the pillows. Then, leaning over her, he combed
his fingers through her hair and fanned it out on the satin
pillowcase. "But I meant everything I said; I'm not making
any promises about the future."

He left the room, but the echo of his words hung in the air,
a dark cloud blocking out all the protests forming in her mind.
She was exhausted, both mentally and physically, but she
knew sleep wouldn't come. A past she had tried to forget had
grown vividly alive and was now threatening the shape of her
future. She got out of bed, slipped into the robe, lifted the
hem and walked to the window, pushing the drapes aside so
she could look out on the patio below. How she hated Jason!
Why couldn't he leave her alone? Why did he have to come

after her? Why did he have to make her feel so weak and ineffectual?

She tried to forget her problems and concentrate on the lawn beyond the patio, where a plump gray-haired Mrs. Smithers was watching Andy on a blanket in the grass. He was waving his hand, trying to catch a butterfly swooping gracefully by. While Linda watched this idyllic scene, Jason strode up and spoke to Mrs. Smithers, who then went into the house. Bending down, Jason picked up Andy, settled him on his lap and began playing a finger-grasping game.

Linda wryly reminded herself of how proud she had been that Andy took so easily to strangers. Now, as she watched him laughing with Jason and reaching for his fingers, she wished that she had taught him to be less friendly. Nothing would have made her happier than to see Andy cry and scream when Jason tried to hold him, but Andy was his usual cheerful self, acting as if he had known Jason forever.

Jason's behavior was far more a mystery to her than Andy's, and she thought back to that evening when she had first met him. He was much older and more sophisticated than the men she had dated back in Kansas, so commanding and self-assured that she couldn't understand why he was even speaking to her. Then, when he told her that he was the president of the largest recording company on the West Coast, she was overwhelmed. She was so intent on getting her big chance that she never stopped to think about what Jason really meant when he offered to take her to a quiet place where he could listen to her sing; she had gone with him willingly. When they were alone and he took her in his arms and began kissing her tenderly, she experienced an insistent surge of emotions she had never known before. He accepted her fervent response as willingness, and by the time she realized what was happening, the situation had gone too far for either of them to stop.

When it was over she had cried in shame, and Jason, rather than soothing her, had berated her for becoming involved in a situation that she couldn't handle. He called her a tease, a spoiled child, said she had deceived him into thinking she was a woman, and that he wished he had never met her. When he had finally rid himself of all his anger and fallen asleep, she stole out of the house, returned to her hotel, packed her bags and left for a small artists' colony she had heard about in Laguna Beach. She was too ashamed to go back to Kansas, and she wanted to get away from Hollywood, where she feared she might run into Jason again.

Laguna Beach was the perfect place to recover from her experience with Jason because the people there helped each other, and when she discovered she was pregnant, her friends offered the emotional support she so desperately needed. She didn't even consider asking for Jason's help because she couldn't risk facing his arrogant denunciations again. She was sure he would blame her for the pregnancy, might even say that she had planned it, so she hid within the artists' colony and managed as best she could.

She had fully expected that Andy would be her responsibility and hers alone. It had never crossed her mind that Jason would ever find out about him, or that, if he did, he would want anything to do with him. His insistent demand for immediate possession of his child had come as a complete shock to her, and this new dimension to his personality had only frightened her more because it showed how little she really knew about the man who was now her husband. How could he be so devoted to his son when he held her, Andy's mother, in such contempt?

And she knew he had nothing but contempt for her. His actions made his attitude perfectly clear. She despised the way he was using his powerful position to force her into submission, but she was determined that this time he wouldn't get what he wanted. She had married him for Andy's sake, but as far as she was concerned, it was a marriage in name only, and she wouldn't let him treat her like a possession, just another object he owned and used.

A rap at the door drew her away from the window. Miss Jenson came in, followed by a tall prim-looking woman in a stiff white uniform. Her dour features seemed to be as heavily starched as her uniform, and Linda felt very uncomfortable when Miss Jenson brought the woman toward her.

"This is Miss Vickers, Andrew's nurse, Mrs. Reynolds. I

thought you should meet her so you could tell her a bit about Andrew.''

Linda began by telling Miss Vickers that Andy was a perfectly healthy and happy child. She mentioned that he was very friendly and enjoyed being with people.

But Miss Vickers was far from impressed with the care he'd been receiving, and as she rose to go she turned to Linda. "Well, I can assure you that from here on I will see that Andrew has a more stable lifestyle. I cannot understand how the son of such a prominent man has been allowed to go about so unprotected. All my previous charges have been carefully guarded against the possibility of kidnappings and the invasion of their privacy, at the very least. You can be assured that I intend to provide young Andrew with the same responsible care.''

Miss Jenson smiled. "Thank you for your time, Mrs. Reynolds. I'm sorry if we've disturbed your rest. Why don't you just get back in bed and try to sleep. I'll take Miss Vickers to meet little Andrew, and then we can be sure that he's in good hands.'' She smiled sweetly, motioning to Miss Vickers, and they left the room.

Linda twisted her hands together; she felt more restless than ever. She wasn't at all sure that Andy would be in good hands with Miss Vickers; she didn't like the woman at all. She walked to the window and saw Miss Vickers take Andy from Jason's arms. Her manner with the baby was completely efficient, and Linda knew that this was just the no-nonsense type of person Jason would want in charge of his son's rearing, not a young scatterbrain, as he imagined her to be. Jason, the baby and his nurse disappeared into the house, and Linda sat down, despondently wishing that she had never agreed to appear in the Pageant of the Masters. But it had seemed like such a harmless idea at the time. How was she to know that Jason was looking for her, that he would see her picture, that he would want custody of his son and be willing to marry her to ensure that custody?

There was a rap at her door; it was Kim, Jason's houseboy and valet. "Your purchases have arrived, Mrs. Reynolds. Would you like me to put them away?"

Linda shook her head. "No, thank you, Kim. Just drop everything on the bed. I'll put them away later. I have nothing else to do."

As soon as Kim left, Linda began unwrapping the packages. There was a large assortment of scanty, lace-trimmed lingerie, and Linda held up one of the sheer silk nightgowns, mentally comparing it with the tailored cotton pajamas she usually slept in. She frowned, realizing that these would have to do until she could get back to Laguna for her own clothing.

The dresses were much more sophisticated than anything she would have bought, but she grimaced and hung them in the closet, smiling happily when she saw some jeans and tee shirts. They were from a small boutique on Rodeo Drive where many movie stars bought their clothing, and they must have cost three times as much as she usually paid for her outfits, but at least they were something she could feel comfortable in. Thank heavens for Southern California's informal atmosphere; even in Beverly Hills, no wardrobe was complete without jeans. She put on a pair of prewashed blue jeans and a striped blue and white vee-necked cotton tee shirt. Then, after slipping into a pair of Mexican leather *huaraches*, she put the rest of her new shoes in the closet. Miss Jenson was certainly efficient, Linda had to admit; she had purchased a complete wardrobe, right down to color-coordinated shoes.

She caught a glimpse of herself as she walked by the mirrored wardrobe doors and twisted the corners of her mouth at the snug fit of the jeans and tee shirt. Very little about her anatomy was left to the imagination, and Linda realized that she would probably never feel comfortable wearing this outfit in public. It might be all right for a glamorous movie star, but it was far too revealing for her own tastes. But it didn't matter now; she was only going to Andy's room, and there wasn't any need for her to dress modestly just to see her nine-month-old son.

She left her room and looked down the carpeted hall, trying to decide which room Andy was in. Then the sounds of splashing water and gurgling laughter took away the guess-work, and she walked down to the nursery, where Miss

Vickers was bathing Andy. Even the nurse's dour expression had been softened by Andy's pleasant personality.

He saw Linda and chortled as he held his chubby little arms out toward her. Linda reached for him, but Miss Vickers lifted him away and wrapped him in a toweling robe.

"Really, Mrs. Reynolds, unannounced visits such as this upset a baby's routine. They cannot be tolerated if I am to instill some discipline into Andrew's life. In addition, since you are recovering from an infection you really shouldn't be around the baby. He might catch it from you."

"Nonsense," Linda said. "Andy is a picture of health; he never gets sick. Besides I feel perfectly fine now. I'm sure I'm over my cold. And let's get something straight: I'm Andy's mother and I won't have you telling me when I can see him. Is that clear, Miss Vickers?"

"Well, I never . . ." Miss Vickers sputtered.

"You have now," Linda said.

Just then Jason came in. He cast a disapproving glance at Linda and went to Andy, chucking him fondly under the chin. Then he turned back to Linda. "Why don't we just let Miss Vickers get on with her work? After all, she's being paid to care for Andrew." He cupped Linda's elbow and propelled her out of the nursery and back to her own room. Then he shut the door, turning her in his arms so she was staring directly into his furious face.

"Just what do you think you were doing in there? I told you to stay in bed."

She returned his glare defiantly. "I don't want to stay in bed. I feel fine, and I wanted to see Andy. I won't have some witchy woman telling me when I can see my own son."

Jason gripped her arms and held her immobile. "Listen carefully. You'll do just as you're told. Miss Vickers comes highly recommended. I'm paying her a good salary, and I don't want you interfering with her when she's trying to do her job. If you want something to do, you might consider your own appearance. Just look at you. These clothes are worse than nothing. You're my wife now. I won't have you wearing that kind of outfit. Every lecher in Hollywood will be trying to get his hands on you. Didn't Miss Jenson get you any clothing?"

Linda smiled at him. "This *is* what Miss Jenson bought me," she said sarcastically, "so if you must blame someone, blame her. Personally," Linda lied, "I don't see anything wrong with this outfit, or would you rather have me running around in your bathrobe?" She twisted out of his arms and moved across the room. "Besides, you needn't worry about an assault on my morality. Only one lecher in Hollywood has ever gotten his hands on me, and you have my assurance that it won't happen again."

The grim look on Jason's face lightened. "Assault . . . lecher . . . really, Linda," he said with a mocking grin, "that's not how I remember it at all. I imagine your memory must be deceiving you. Perhaps it needs some refreshing?"

He strode over to her and pulled her against his body. She strained to get away from him, but he tightened his hold, forcing her arms behind her back and gripping them easily with one hand. His other hand cupped her chin and raised her face toward his. Then his lips descended on hers with an indomitable need to conquer. His hand left her chin and began stroking her hip, pressing her to his body until she felt the surging strength of his rising desire.

She tried to remain calm and detached, but her flesh began tingling with the same pulsating hunger Jason's touch had sent racing through it on the first night they met. When her lips softened and parted, his became tender, as if he were savoring both the victory and her passionate response. He released her arms and she brought them up to encircle his neck, letting her fingers comb through the short curling hairs just above his collar. When she sighed with contentment, Jason stood back, holding her at arm's length while his mocking eyes surveyed her parted lips and heaving breasts.

His lips twisted in a taunting grin and his hand came up to gently push a stray lock back from her face as he continued to study her. "I think it only fair to warn you," he whispered, "that you don't have *my* assurance that this won't happen again. . . . You don't have it at all. But this isn't the time; I have a dinner engagement. I'll tell Mrs. Smithers to serve you in your room. Then I expect you to get some rest. And when you're feeling better, perhaps we can have dinner together. I'm sure you're anxious to meet some of my friends."

She couldn't stand the way he was mocking her. After all this time, after all her vows, she had melted in his hands like a piece of warm taffy. She hated herself almost as much as she hated him. "I don't want to meet your friends. In fact, I wish I'd never met you. The night we met was the blackest moment of my life."

Jason quirked his brow. "Really, my dear. How fortunate for Andrew that I found him when I did. At least now he'll have one parent who fondly remembers the evening of his conception." He strode from the room and the echo of his arrogant laughter vibrated painfully in Linda's ears.

In a short while she heard the sound of his car driving away from the house. Then Mrs. Smithers brought her dinner. After eating, she changed into one of her new nightgowns and fell almost immediately into an exhausted sleep.

Chapter Three

Apparently Jason was right about Linda having gotten out of bed too soon, because the following morning she was more exhausted than ever, and for the next few days she slept almost constantly. Finally, almost a week after Jason had brought her to his home, she awoke feeling thoroughly refreshed and healthy. The bright sunshine streaming through the window reflected her own sparkling joy, and though she couldn't explain *why* her spirits had suddenly risen, she decided not to question this new development. She bounded out of bed, showered and dressed quickly, then went to the nursery to see Andy. As she peeked through the door Miss Vickers held a finger across her lips, indicating that he was still sleeping. Nodding, Linda backed out of the room and closed the door softly behind her. She'd have her breakfast while Andy napped.

The downstairs layout was a mystery to her because when Jason had brought her here a week ago he had carried her directly to her bedroom, and this was not the house he had lived in a year and a half ago. She hesitated for a moment at the bottom of the stairway. Then she followed the tantalizing scent of freshly brewed coffee and found Mrs. Smithers setting up a breakfast tray in the kitchen.

"Mrs. Reynolds, what are you doing here? I was just preparing your tray. Mr. Reynolds said you'd be having your meals in bed."

Linda smiled. "There's no need for that. I'm feeling much better, and I'm perfectly capable of coming down for my meals. You don't have to climb stairs for me."

Mrs. Smithers waved her hand. "It's no trouble. Mr.

Reynolds has gone and won't be home until dinner, so I have the whole day to myself. But if you prefer to be downstairs, why don't you go into the breakfast room and I'll serve you there? Would you like bacon or sausage with your eggs?"

"Bacon would be fine, Mrs. Smithers," Linda said, as she walked through a white louvered door leading to a breakfast room that resembled a country greenhouse.

A great bow window, curving into the garden, overlooked an expanse of lush tropical plants, while huge baskets of colorful orchids hanging from the ceiling flooded the room with a brilliant floral rainbow. Fragile green ferns swayed gently beneath the orchids, cooling the iridescent intensity with their pale delicacy, and the drifting fronds of potted palms reached toward the ceiling, adding their stately splendor to this indoor garden paradise.

Mrs. Smithers came in while Linda was admiring the idyllic beauty of the room. "It's lovely, isn't it? Of all the rooms in the house I like it best," she said as she placed Linda's tray on the round, glass-topped table. "Now, you just sit down and enjoy your breakfast. I'm glad you're feeling better. Mr. Reynolds has been very concerned about you; he'll be so pleased to see you up and around." She smiled and left the room.

Linda walked across the ceramic-tiled floor and drew a white wrought-iron chair up to the table where Mrs. Smithers had placed her tray. Jason was concerned about her? He'd be pleased to see her feeling good? Hmmph. Was she the only one who knew the truth about the man? Jason was only interested in her because he wanted his son, and he knew she'd never give Andy up without a fight. A fight was exactly what he'd get from her anyway; even if she was his wife, even if she was living in his home, she'd never forgive him for the way he had treated her, and he'd never get a second chance to laugh at her.

But fighting Jason would take strength, so she picked up her fork and began eating. The food was delicious, and once again she was surprised at how hungry she was, despite the upheavals her life had undergone. When she had finished, she brought the tray into the kitchen, rinsed her dishes and put them in the dishwasher. Mrs. Smithers returned just as she was dropping the last spoon into the machine.

"Mrs. Reynolds, you shouldn't be doing that. Mr. Reynolds wants you to rest. Besides, that's my job."

Linda waved her hand. "Nonsense. I feel fine, and I don't expect to be waited on; I'm used to doing things myself." She had no intention of becoming the helpless naïf Jason wanted her to be. He might think he knew her, but she'd show him just how much he had to learn.

She left Mrs. Smithers and went back to the nursery. Andy was in the playpen, and Miss Vickers was tidying up the room. Linda walked in and picked up Andy. "It's such a lovely day, Miss Vickers; I think I'll take Andy out for some fresh air."

Miss Vickers looked at her coldly. "I think not, Mrs. Reynolds. I intend to take Andrew out this afternoon; I don't believe in taking children out before lunch. Andrew can stay indoors for now."

Linda narrowed her eyes at Miss Vickers. She didn't care what Jason thought about the prim and proper nurse, she hated her. Maybe this was the time to take a stand and let Jason know that his opinions weren't the only ones that mattered. "I'm going to take Andy out right now, and furthermore I'll take him out any time I please. I told you; I'm his mother, and I won't have you dictate when I may and may not see my son."

Miss Vickers' thin lips grew taut, and she glared at Linda. "Mr. Reynolds assured me that I'd have complete control over Andrew's care. I cannot work here if I am to be subjected to your constant interference. I intend to speak to Mr. Reynolds about this, and if the situation doesn't change, I shall resign."

Linda picked up Andy's blue sweater and cap. "Well, then, we'd better say good-bye right now, because I don't intend to let you come between me and my son." She strode angrily from the room and down the stairway to the front entrance. A station wagon was parked in front of the house, and Linda, discovering that the keys were in the ignition, settled Andy in the baby seat she had brought from the nursery, started the engine and sped down the driveway. Noting that the gas tank was full, she drove onto the San Diego Freeway and headed south.

In seventy-five minutes she had exited at Laguna Canyon and was on her way to the small rented house where Andy and she had lived. She opened the door and was shocked to find that none of her personal things were there. Except for the furniture that came with the house, the cottage was bare. She walked through the rooms in a trancelike state of dazed disbelief. She felt that a part of her had disappeared; the cottage was now just an empty house, with no sign that it once had been her home, Andy's home. Something quivered in the pit of her stomach and she felt strangely bereft, as if someone had deliberately eradicated this link with her past, as if someone wanted her to forget that this part of her life had ever existed. And she had no doubt as to who that someone was. Jason's domineering presence had followed her even here. Shivering in the eerie silence of the deserted house, she closed the door and walked down the street to see Mrs. Mason.

Mrs. Mason greeted her with a smile and reached for Andy. "Linda, it's so good to see you. You look so well, better than you have in a long time. I didn't expect to see you again after your husband sent those movers to pack up your things. They said you wouldn't be back."

Linda walked into the living room, sat down on the colonial-style sofa and ran her fingers along the edges of the wide maple arms. "Why don't we put Andy down for a nap? He's tired, and there are some things I'd like to discuss with you."

When Andy had been comfortably settled in the bedroom, Linda and Mrs. Mason sat at the old kitchen table chatting over sweet buns and coffee.

The older woman tilted her head as she looked at Linda. "You look rested, Linda, but you don't look happy. Is anything wrong?"

Linda hesitated for a moment, then told Mrs. Mason about her problem with Miss Vickers. "Jason wants only the best for Andy, and he thinks very highly of Miss Vickers. But I don't like her; she's too cold. There's more to caring for a child than just seeing to his physical needs, and besides, I can't stand the thought of needing her permission to see Andy."

Mrs. Mason nodded in agreement. "I understand how you feel. I think you ought to tell your husband. You say he wants only the best for little Andy, so surely he'd understand your concern."

Linda reflected for a moment. "Mrs. Mason, would you be willing to live with us for a while? Andy knows you, and you understand how much he means to me. You'd be the perfect replacement for Miss Vickers."

Mrs. Mason shook her head doubtfully. "I'd love to be with you and Andy. You can't imagine how lonely it's been since you left. But what will your husband say? I'm not a professional nurse."

Linda smiled. "Don't worry about that. You love Andy, and the warmth that comes from that love will mean more to him than anything else. Let's get your things together. I imagine Miss Vickers has complained to Jason by now, and he's probably as angry as a hornet with a broken nest. The sooner we get Andy home, the easier things will be."

Linda hadn't mistaken Jason's mood. He came dashing down the stone steps even before the station wagon had stopped, and his usually impassive features were contorted by unrestrained anger. The car had barely stopped when he opened Linda's door, grasped her elbow and pulled her out of the car. "Where were you? Everyone's been in an uproar. Miss Vickers left in a huff, saying she wouldn't work where her authority was challenged. We went looking for you, but you'd driven off in Miss Jenson's station wagon without telling anyone where you were going. What the devil is going on?"

Jason's outburst didn't surprise Linda; she remembered how enraged he had been that night after they had made love. But this time she wasn't afraid; his overt anger didn't frighten her nearly as much as his cold, emotionless attacks, and she calmly removed his hand from her arm. "If we have something to discuss, I suggest we do it in private. Mrs. Mason is with me, and she can take Andy upstairs. There's no reason for them to be subjected to all of this."

Jason stared in open-mouthed amazement while Linda led Mrs. Mason and Andy into the house. Then he plunged his hands into his pockets, followed them up to the nursery and waited silently while Linda and Mrs. Mason looked around to see where everything was. Their exploration seemed to him to take forever. Finally, when his patience was completely exhausted, he grasped Linda's elbow, placed her firmly in front of him and propelled her out of the nursery and into the master bedroom, where he slammed the door behind him.

Turning her toward him, he gripped her shoulders in his large, muscular hands. "Now, suppose you tell me what this is all about?"

Linda tried to free herself, but he refused to loosen his grip, and she finally gave up. "I don't know what you mean. I just took Andy for a ride to see Mrs. Mason. He misses her, and so do I." When Jason relaxed his hold, she twisted away and walked to the window.

"Why did Miss Vickers leave?" Jason asked. "What did you say to her?"

"I told her that she wasn't going to tell me when I could see Andy."

Jason walked to the window and turned her toward him. "She came highly recommended. She was hired to care for Andrew, and you shouldn't have interfered."

"I'm his mother. How could anything I do be called interference? Anyway, I'm glad she left. I don't care how highly recommended she was, I thought she was a heartless old witch and I didn't want her around Andy. Mrs. Mason's going to stay and look after him, at least for a while. He likes her, and so do I. Besides, she would never tell me that I couldn't see my own son."

Jason's usual calm demeanor had returned, and his emotions were once again under control. "All right, if that's what you want, Mrs. Mason can stay. But don't think I'll tolerate any slipshod treatment where Andrew is concerned."

"And you think I would?" Actually, right now Linda didn't care what Jason thought; she was too exhausted from the drive to Laguna. But it was worth it: Miss Vickers was out, Mrs. Mason was in, and Jason knew that he wasn't going to have the only say about Andy's care.

"I most certainly do. I didn't consider that shack in Laguna the best home for a growing child."

"The house was merely a matter of economics. It was all I could afford at the time."

"But it wasn't all *I* could afford."

"You weren't paying my bills."

"And whose fault was that?" Jason asked, pulling her to him. "You could have had anything you wanted, everything you needed, but you chose not to come to me. Why, Linda? Why?" His smoldering black eyes narrowed with pain and searched her startled face.

She tried to turn away; his eyes were embers on her flesh, but his hand cupped her chin, making her submit to his scrutiny. They stood there for what seemed like an eternity, but Linda couldn't move; she was being torn apart by a mind that wanted to escape and a body that wanted to edge closer. Jason's hand tightened beneath her chin and brought her mouth up to his; his lips touched hers lightly in a gentle, tentative kiss. His hand left her chin and moved to her back, sensuously stroking her spine and drawing her closer into the circle of his arms.

Linda felt her senses reeling. The surging desire blossoming within her radiated to the depths of her body. She remembered this weak, mindless sensation and knew that, once again, Jason's touch had made her body a traitor to her vows. She tried to block out the havoc his hands were wreaking on her skin by recalling the vicious accusations he had hurled at her. She steeled herself to be stiff and unresponsive, but he took this as a challenge and pressed his mouth more firmly onto hers, forcing her lips apart with a passionate ferocity that threatened to consume her.

Suddenly, just when she felt the remnants of her control shriveling beneath the heat of his embrace, he released her and pushed her away. "Good God, you are made of ice, aren't you? I'd get more reaction from a block of wood." His voice was ragged as he ran his fingers through his dark hair.

Linda turned away so that he couldn't see the torment on her face. Her breath caught in her throat as she tried to gain control over her careening heartbeat; she was so confused that she couldn't trust herself to speak or to look at Jason. She didn't understand how, after knowing all she did about Jason, she could still let herself bask in the sun of his caress. She wanted to press her body to his and feel his hands and lips against her flesh, but she couldn't let him know how weak she was; he respected only strength. She took a deep breath, fought down her own physical responses and tried to appear calm and disinterested, completely uninvolved.

"That's exactly how I feel when you touch me, Jason, like a block of wood. I warned you that I've changed. Don't come looking for the girl you used to know. She *was* too dumb to take care of herself; I recall that as one of the milder accusations you hurled at me that night. Well, now I know exactly what I want, and my wishbook doesn't include you."

"Is that so?" Jason crossed his arms, and his gaze moved slowly down her body, then drifted to the bed. "Why is it that I don't believe you? Why do I feel that, given enough time, I could carve through that block of wood and find the soft, sweet girl you used to be?" He smiled smugly.

Linda backed away. "Don't come near me."

"Don't worry, I'm not about to give you another chance to be a martyr. I've heard enough about my taking advantage of your untouched innocence. I'm not going to let you play that scene again. I can wait; I'm not that desperate. But I wonder about you. I have a very good memory, and I can't forget how passionate you were when I held you in my arms." He narrowed his eyes, then turned and walked slowly out of the room.

An uncontrollable shiver vibrated through Linda's body and she raced into her own bedroom, slamming the door between their rooms as if to shut him out of her life. She went into the bathroom, turned on the cold water and splashed it on her flaming cheeks, but there was no way she could slake the fire blazing deep within her. Much as the thought frightened her, she had to admit that Jason was right: she didn't have enough willpower to resist him forever. Yet she *couldn't* give in; she never again wanted to experience the misery of Jason's disdain, and no matter how contemptuously he thought of her now, it would be ten times worse if she ever again let herself share his bed.

Returning to the bedroom, she sank into the chaise longue, closed her eyes, put her feet up and tried to relax her quivering nerves. After a while her heart slowed to its normal pace and the lonely silence of her bedroom became too confining to bear. Solitude gave her time to think, and she didn't want to think; her thoughts were too disturbing, and she knew that any conclusion she reached would only upset her more. From the first moment she had seen Jason she had felt an attraction such as she had never before experienced, yet she knew that he thought of her as some sort of toy, an object created for his amusement. She rejected that role and despised him for picturing her that way, but yet . . . She didn't want to think about it; she just didn't want to think about it. She rose from her seat and smoothed her clothing, brushing off her jeans and pulling her tee shirt down tautly over her breasts.

She left her bedroom and walked down the corridor to the nursery. Never before had she felt such a need to hold Andy and look into his dark, laughing eyes. It was almost as if all the love she and Jason might have shared had gone into the creation of their son. How wonderful it would be if Andy had been the result of an everlasting love, rather than a night of wild desire which she herself could not yet understand. But that was too much to hope for, and for Andy's sake she would have to learn to live with the harsh reality of her new life.

Mrs. Mason was feeding Andy, and he grinned, holding his arms up to Linda, when she entered the room.

"I'll finish feeding him," Linda said. "Why don't you go downstairs and get a cup of tea? If Mrs. Smithers is there I'm sure you'll enjoy chatting with her."

"I could do with a bit of something," Mrs. Mason said, "if you're sure it will be all right. I don't want to step on any toes."

"I'm positive," Linda said. "Mrs. Smithers is a dear; she'll be delighted with your company. Now, go on, Andy is clamoring for another mouthful."

Just as she had known it would, Andy's cheerful personality made her forget her problems, and by the time she had wiped his face and hands and changed his diaper she was singing and laughing with him. She put him in his crib and rubbed her hand slowly over his warm back as she hummed a lullaby. Within minutes his even breathing told her that he had fallen asleep, so she covered him and turned to leave the room. Her fingers flew to her open mouth, stifling an involuntary gasp. Jason was leaning in the doorway, his arms folded nonchalantly across his chest, a cynical smile playing about the corners of his mouth.

Linda's voice was husky and uneven. "How long have you been here?"

"Long enough," he said. "I met Mrs. Mason when she was going downstairs, and I asked who was watching Andrew. Actually, I wanted to see him myself, but you two seemed to be getting on so fabulously that I didn't want to interrupt. Perhaps next time you'll invite me in. After all, a boy needs a father, doesn't he?"

"That depends on the father," Linda said.

"Just what is that supposed to mean?"

"It means that a biological accident doesn't make a man a father."

"A biological accident? Is that what my son is?"

"Stop twisting my words. You didn't even know about your son until a few days ago."

"And whose fault was that?"

"Mine. And if I had my way you'd *never* have known about him."

She stormed into the hall with Jason following after her. Mrs. Mason was coming up the stairway, and Linda told her that Andy was settled for the night. The older woman thanked Linda and went into the nursery. Linda entered her own room and tried to shut the door, but Jason's broad hand stopped it and held it open until he came in behind her.

She whirled to face him. "What is it, Jason? What do you want now?"

"You're not a very good loser, are you? Well, don't worry, I'm a modest winner. I won't make you grovel; we can still be friends. In fact, I only wanted to tell you that we have a dinner date tonight; we're dining with friends. I hope you plan on wearing something else besides that." He indicated her jeans. "Around here we dress for dinner."

"I don't want to be your friend, and I don't want to meet your friends. We're married only because of Andy; there's no reason for us to socialize. And speaking of clothing, what right did you have to take everything from my house in Laguna? There were things I wanted. They were my property, you know."

"Your guitar is in your closet. I thought you might want it handy. Everything else is in the garage; I had it all brought here for your convenience. I didn't think you'd be returning to Laguna Beach so soon. You can take whatever you want, although I don't think you'll need anything. Andrew's nursery is pretty complete, and we can buy whatever's missing." He took a deep breath. "Now, let's get something straight. It's true that we married for Andrew's sake, but that doesn't alter the fact that we *are* married, and I expect you to behave just like any other wife; that includes socializing with my friends. Do I make myself clear?"

"Perfectly clear. But why? We have nothing in common. You won't enjoy my company any more than I'll enjoy yours."

"We have Andrew in common, and social relationships as well as marriages have been based on a lot less, so I don't want to hear any more arguments from you. Just get dressed. I'll meet you for a drink in the library in an hour."

Linda stared after him as he walked into the adjoining room, then wrinkled her nose at the already closed door. It was a futile gesture which in no way lessened the fact that, once again, Jason had won. As always, she was going to do what he wanted. He held the trump card, a custody battle for Andy, and unless they began playing with a new deck, there was no way she could win. Sighing with exasperation, she went into the bathroom and turned on the shower. Tilting her head, she arched her body to welcome the pulsating stream of warmth that flowed over her. If only she could stay there forever.

What if she could defy Jason, find a way to fight him on his own terms? But that was impossible. She knew that he had meant everything he said. If she wasn't in the library within the hour, she was sure he would come looking for her, and what was the point of another confrontation? It was senseless to provoke a battle which she was destined to lose. Opening her eyes, she soaped her body with a speed and firmness that indicated her unwilling return to the demands of reality. Then, after a quick rinse in a stream of cooler water, she stepped onto the thick carpet, took a warm towel from the heated rack and began drying herself.

She was wearing lacy bikini lingerie and looking through her closet when the door to the adjoining bedroom opened. She snatched a dress, still on its hanger, and held it in front of her. "Would you please put a lock on that door so I can get some privacy?"

Jason's shirt hung half open, revealing the dark, curling hair beneath it. He fumbled with the lower buttons as he walked toward her, a grim look on his aquiline features. "No locked doors between us—ever." His hand shot out and grasped hers, releasing the dress and sending it swaying back into the closet. She struggled to free her hand so she could use it as a shield, but he tightened his grip and she could only cringe helplessly while his eyes ravished her body.

"As for your coveted privacy, I imagine the fact that you don't share my bed or even my room gives you more privacy than most wives would ever want. Depriving me of these few random glimpses would be unnecessarily cruel." He spoke with mocking humor.

As he drew closer, the spicy scent of his after-shave penetrated her nostrils and sent shivers racing up her spine. Her breathing quickened, and her lips parted with desire while her mind alerted her to the vulnerability of her position. But, vulnerable or not, this was one battle Jason wasn't going to win. Her pride demanded this small victory, at least. She clenched her fists and drew farther into the closet, forcing herself to speak in a carefully controlled voice. "Did you want something, Jason?"

His smoldering eyes lifted to her face and glinted with undisguised amusement when he noted the taut determination of her features. "Need you ask? I thought you knew what I wanted and were dead set on stopping me from getting it." He tried to pull her to him, but she ducked out of range and moved to the side, glaring at him like a cornered vixen.

He laughed. "You have a lot to learn about being a wife. You'll just have to stop thinking about sex every time I come near you. I may want you for something else . . . occasionally." He smiled cynically and held out his hand. "Kim's been busy running errands, and I can't fasten these without help." A pair of gold cufflinks rested in his palm. "Would helping me with these be an infringement on your privacy?"

"No, of course not." She took the cufflinks and Jason held out his wrists. She lowered her head both to fasten the studs and to hide the flames that were coloring her cheeks. He had made her feel like a mean little child. Why did she have to snap at him? It was just that he was always so self-assured that she had never thought he would need her help with anything. Her hands trembled as she fumbled with the soft silk cuffs, and his breath warmed her nape as she bent to complete her task. When she was finished she turned back to the closet, too tense to look at Jason.

He came up behind her, put his hands on either side of her waist and drew her body back against his. His fingers meshed and flexed over her abdomen, gently kneading the flesh that they covered. "Now, that wasn't so bad, was it?"

"No." Her voice was a husky whisper.

He lowered his head, feathering his lips over the side of her neck. She arched her body as his mouth moved to the curve of her chin and sought the corner of her mouth. Instinctively she shifted in his arms until their lips were fully mated. At first his kiss was gentle, his lips barely touching hers as they softly grazed and teased; then it became more demanding as his tongue parted her lips and sought the company of hers. She felt herself drowning, caught in a vortex of passion she was still afraid to enter; then, gasping for air, she pressed her palms against his chest and leaned back, gazing up at him. Her uneven breath escaped through her softly parted lips.

Jason's eyes met hers. "Maybe you're right. Maybe it's not important for you to meet my friends. Right now, I don't have much interest in them myself." His hands cupped her face and his thumbs stroked her pulsing temples.

Once again she felt the whirlpool spinning, drawing her into an emotional situation she couldn't control. She looked at Jason as he smiled down at her. She wanted to trust him, but she just couldn't, not now, not when she remembered how quickly that smile could change to a sneer.

"No, Jason." She shook her head. "I meant what I said. I'll help with your cufflinks, but that's as far as it goes. If you want us to spend the evening together, we might as well go to dinner."

Jason's thumbs slipped to her cheeks and teased them with little circling motions. Tilting his head to the side, he studied her reaction. She took a deep breath and caught her lower lip with her teeth. If he forced her into anything now she'd never forgive him—not ever. And not even for Andy's sake would she make herself stay here in Jason's home.

He must have sensed how strongly she felt, because he lowered his hands and rubbed them slowly over her wrists. "Hurry and get dressed; I'll meet you in the library." He turned her toward the closet, patted her backside and strode out of the room.

Linda sighed. She had succeeded. This time, at least, she had shown Jason that her feelings mattered, and that he had to consider them if he really wanted to make their marriage, such as it was, work. She felt good, better than she had in a long time, and she wanted to go out, to celebrate her victory. Small though it might be, it was the second time today that Jason hadn't insisted on having his own way.

Flipping through the hangers, she admired the clothing Miss Jenson had chosen for her. Everything was so beautiful that it was hard to make a choice, but she finally slipped into a short, knife-pleated, blue chiffon dress. Glancing in the mirror, she was pleased with the way the high jeweled neckline and fitted bodice clung to the curves of her breasts while the sharp pleats swung freely over her long slender legs. She put on a pair of high-heeled sandals and ran a comb through her hair. Her hour was already up, but she didn't care; she wasn't leaving without seeing Andy.

Her mouth opened in surprise when she walked into the nursery and saw Jason holding Andy on his lap, tickling him under the chin. Andy was laughing and reaching for Jason's fingers as they moved away, then returned for another surprise attack. For a moment the undeniable similarity between the two smiling faces made Linda cringe with guilt about what she had done. She had been so sure that Jason wouldn't want her child that she had never considered the possibility of the loving relationship she was seeing now. How could she? It wasn't like Jason. Still, what did she really know about Jason Reynolds, the man who was now her husband, beyond what the newspapers had told her?

"What happened?" she asked. "I thought Andy was sleeping."

"He was, but he woke up," Jason said. "Teething pains, according to Mrs. Mason. She gave him a bottle."

"You'd better be careful. Sometimes he spits up after having his bottle."

Jason shrugged. "It doesn't matter. I offered to stay with him while Mrs. Mason got a book from the library. Andrew and I have a lot to learn about each other, and I don't want to waste any time. Don't worry about my clothes. I have other suits, but I have only one son. A suit can be replaced, but what price do you put on a child's growth?" His voice was low, almost as if he were talking to himself. Then he smiled and walked toward Linda. "Say hello to your mother, Andrew," he said as Andy held out his hands. Linda took him in her arms and was kissing him when Mrs. Mason returned.

Mrs. Mason looked at them and smiled. "It's good to see you all together. Andy needs a mother *and* a father. It wasn't right, Linda, you trying to raise Andy by yourself. He needs two parents; no one can replace a father."

"My feelings exactly," Jason said, reaching out to take Andy from Linda. He kissed him on the cheek, then handed him to Mrs. Mason. "We'd better leave," he said to Linda, "or we'll be late. I've spent so much time in the nursery that there's no time for that drink I promised you."

Linda shook her head. "It doesn't matter. I enjoyed being with Andy; the drink wasn't that important."

Jason narrowed his eyes as he opened her car door a few minutes later. Leaning against the roof, he grinned. "I've been thinking about what you said a few minutes ago and I agree; it's much more intimate to share a child than a drink. I'm glad we spent the time together . . . just like an ordinary family, wouldn't you say?" Without waiting for her answer, he helped her in, closed her door and walked around to the driver's side.

He drove down Benedict Canyon Road and named the famous owners of each gated estate. He pointed out one large piece of property which used to belong to a famous silent movie star and told Linda that it had just been sold to a real estate developer who would probably subdivide it, since it was now so expensive to run that no one person could afford the upkeep.

Linda admired the beautiful trees that shielded each side street with a graceful green canopy, and Jason told her that the streets in Beverly Hills had been carefully planned. Each one was bordered with a different type of tree, which was the only one allowed on that particular street. Linda thought that the maple trees were especially beautiful.

When they turned onto Wilshire Boulevard, the area became more commercial and the large estates were replaced by shops, theaters and restaurants. Jason drove along Wilshire until he reached La Cienega Boulevard—Restaurant Row. He stopped the car in front of a long red canopy and a doorman stepped forward to open Linda's door, while a parking attendant did the same for Jason. Then Jason moved swiftly to stand behind Linda and, placing his hand possessively on her waist, led her into the restaurant.

The owner greeted them and showed them to a private dining room at the side of the restaurant. Two couples were already seated at the table. The men stood when they walked in, and Jason made the introductions. Alan Shelton was one of television's most successful producers; at least one of his shows was usually rated within the top ten. His wife, Barbara, was the lead actress in a popular comedy series. The other people at the table were Ken and Cindy Stone, whom Linda had already met.

"You have to try the chili," Ken said to Linda when the waiter came to take their order. "That is, if you like chili; Marge makes the world's best chili."

"I love chili," Linda said.

"We'll start with a tray of cracked crab and oysters on a bed of ice, then why don't you bring us all small bowls of chili?" Jason said without even looking at the menu. "It just doesn't feel right to come here and not have the chili. Next, I think we'd better have something more substantial. What about Beef Wellington all around?"

Everyone agreed with Jason's choices, and the waiter left the room.

"Have you had a chance to get to the shops yet?" Barbara asked Linda.

"No, I've just been lounging around, taking things easy. I've never been much of a clothes horse."

Barbara raised her eyebrows. "Well, we'll have to change that. Once you've seen the shops on Rodeo Drive you won't know what to buy first."

Jason laughed and placed his hand over Linda's. "Stop that, will you, Barbara? I like Linda just the way she is. If she starts visiting your little boutiques, she'll break me."

Alan laughed. "That'll be the day. Jason, you've got more money than you know what to do with. It's about time you joined the ranks of us harried husbands." He turned to Linda. "Don't believe a word he says, Linda. Let Barbara show you around; enjoy yourself. Only, please, make sure Barbara doesn't spend too much money. I'm not as rich as Jason."

Linda smiled, then wrinkled her nose as she sniffed the sickeningly sweet odor of a flowery perfume. Turning, she looked at the woman standing in the doorway.

"There you are. Marge said I'd find you in here." The tall platinum blonde floated into the room, motioned to the men to remain seated, then drifted over to Jason and planted a proprietary kiss on his cheek. The low vee of her white halter-necked dress gaped when she bent over, giving the entire table an unobstructed view of her abundant female charms. She rested her hand possessively on Jason's shoulder and looked at Linda. "And this must be your carefully hidden wife. How nice it is to meet you at last." Her hand undulated down Jason's shoulder and onto his chest. "Jason is a man of many surprises . . . some of them more interesting than others."

Linda pressed her fists into her thighs as she watched the blonde's sensuous movements. The woman made her feel about as interesting as an empty paper sack. Was this one of the sophisticated women Jason had thrown up to her? Absolutely. It had to be. There isn't one inexperienced bone in her entire body, Linda thought wryly. And she certainly wasn't a stranger; if she wasn't his sister or his mother, then they shared an intimate relationship Linda didn't want to think about.

Her teeth ground silently against each other as she watched Jason. He looked so contented that she expected him to purr. She, on the other hand, felt like snarling. She looked down at the table and had to stop herself from lifting two ice-filled waterglasses and dumping them over Jason and his charming friend. That would cool them off in more ways than one. She smiled at the mental image of dripping platinum hair and running mascara—if only she had enough nerve to make it a reality.

Jason was acting as if she were invisible, as if she didn't exist. And he was the one who had said he wanted a normal marriage! Ha! Even in Tinsel Town *this* little arrangement couldn't be considered normal.

Jason's mouth curved in amusement as he raised his hand to grasp the red-tipped fingers that had returned to his shoulder. "Linda, I'd like you to meet Monique Le Paige, latest discovery of JMR Productions." He held Monique's hand within the circle of his.

Meet Monique, Linda thought, just like that, as if the statuesque blonde were just another employee, like Kim or Mrs. Smithers. Did he really think she was that naïve? She looked back at the icewater and decided that she'd rather use a couple of gooey whipped cream pies to wipe the complacent smirks off their faces—water wasn't messy enough. But Jason wanted sophistication, didn't he? Well, she was a fast learner. Her lips widened in a Cheshire-cat smile. "I'm glad to meet you, Miss Le Paige." No childish tantrums, she warned herself; just play this scene as coolly as the rest of them.

"Monique, please." The blonde flashed her perfectly capped teeth. "I'm too good a friend of the family for such formality."

Linda smiled back so broadly that she thought her cheeks would crack. She didn't have to ask which member of the family Monique was so friendly with.

Finally Monique sighed and released Jason's shoulder. "I've got to get back. My date will think I've left him for good." She smiled alluringly at him. "I'll see you tomorrow, darling, at the studio." She wafted through the door. She had made the studio sound like their secluded trysting place.

The flowery scent of her perfume hung over the room like a funeral wreath. Monique was attractive enough to be a threat to any woman, and Linda could see Barbara and Cindy eyeing their own husbands, grateful that she hadn't made a play for one of them. When they turned their sympathetic glances toward her, she compressed her lips and threw back her shoulders. Jason had done it again; he had made her feel like some worthless piece of dirt. He hadn't even considered her feelings when he played public pattycake with his mistress.

Well, if he didn't care, neither would she. She wasn't going to let him upset her anymore. He and Monique could both go to the devil for all she cared. In fact, she would pay for their one-way tickets.

The waiter brought the food, and she reached for her fork, determined not to let Jason ruin her evening, but even her best efforts couldn't help her to work up an appetite, and the world-famous chili stuck in her throat like a mouthful of sawdust.

For the rest of the evening Linda was concentrating so hard on convincing everyone that Monique hadn't bothered her that she hardly remembered what they had discussed. She was exhausted, and she couldn't wait to get home and be alone so she could drop the phony smile that was making her face ache.

At last they said goodnight and she slid into the Mercedes, thankful that the trip home was a short one. Her efforts to hide her embarrassment had been an emotional drain, and the last person she wanted to see or talk to was Jason; after all, he could have stopped Monique if he had wanted to. But it was obvious he hadn't wanted to; he had been enjoying himself too much. Leaning back, Linda closed her eyes and pretended to be asleep.

Jason whistled softly to himself as he tipped the parking attendant and settled himself behind the wheel. "Are you tired?" he asked, moving the car away from the curb and into the stream of traffic.

Linda nodded mutely. She had nothing to say to him, nothing he'd want to hear. She needed some time to herself, time to think, to sort out her feelings and get them under control. She wasn't ready to take on Jason, not yet. Folding her hands in her lap, she forced herself to take long, deep breaths in the hope that Jason would think she had fallen asleep.

Then she realized that, no matter what he thought, he wasn't going to leave her alone. His hand moved gently down her arm, and when he reached her wrist, his massaging strokes became probing tentacles, picking at the meshed network of her fingers until he had loosened their desperate grip. Then, grasping her hand, he raised it to his lips and kissed the curving lines of her palm.

Linda's eyelids tightened and she tried to stop the weakening sensation that was fluttering in the pit of her stomach. She couldn't accept the ease with which Jason moved from one woman to another. She didn't care how naïve he thought she was, he wasn't going to use her to satisfy an appetite that Monique had created. Sitting up abruptly, she snatched her hand away with a snort of disgust.

He turned toward her, raising his eyebrows quizzically. "I thought you were sleeping."

"I was, until I felt something on my hand." She grimaced and wiped her palm with a tissue.

Jason's mouth quirked in a humorless smile as he opened the electronically controlled gate. Two German shepherds ran toward the car until they were called back by a watchman. Jason waved to him and stopped the car by the front steps.

Linda didn't wait for him to open her door. As soon as he had turned off the ignition, she released the latch and swung out of the car. She raced up the steps, expecting him to follow her, but he stayed behind to speak with the watchman. She ran into her room and closed her door, but there was no point in locking it because Jason would just use the one between their rooms. She thought about blocking the adjoining door with a piece of furniture, but she doubted if she could move anything heavy enough, and besides, she didn't want him to think that she was afraid to face him; he would only use that fear to his advantage.

She would just get ready for bed as if nothing had happened. She took off her dress, hung it in the closet and began tissuing off her makeup. She had used one tissue and was reaching for another when she found the box empty. She didn't wear much makeup, but still she had to get it off before going to bed. She looked at the door leading to Jason's room. Why not? What better way to show him that she wasn't afraid? She put on a robe and opened the door without knocking. What's sauce for the goose, she thought.

Jason turned from the mirror where he was unbuttoning his shirt. "Well, this is an unexpected pleasure." He pulled off his shirt and tossed it onto a brown leather club chair. His tanned chest glistened beneath a mat of short, curling hair.

"I need some tissues." She avoided his eyes and looked for the bathroom.

"Oh," he said softly. "I thought you might have some other needs."

She wrinkled her nose and headed for the bathroom. "None that you could satisfy. The only thing I need from you is tissues."

"Is that so?" He rested his arms on the doorjamb, trapping her in the bathroom.

"Exactly so. Now, if you'll excuse me?" She tried to slip under his arm. "Please, Jason, I have some things I want to do before I go to sleep."

"Funny, so do I. Maybe we can do them together." He lowered his arm, blocking her escape.

"You can wash your own face."

"That's not what I had in mind."

"Too bad, because that's all I'm going to do." She gripped his arm and tried to shift it out of her way. It was immovable, an imprisoning steel bar.

"You're sure?"

"Positive."

"Well, if you're going to wash it off anyway, it doesn't matter if I kiss some of your makeup off first, does it?"

She backed into the bathroom, stopping only when the backs of her legs encountered the side of the tub. "Don't touch me."

"You don't mean that."

"I do, I really do. Don't come any closer." She looked for something to throw, pulled a towel off the rack and tossed it at him.

He ducked, then lunged forward to grab her waist. "What are you going to do now?" He gripped the fists that were aimed at his chest.

"I hate you."

"But I'm still your husband."

"Only when it suits your purposes."

"Like now." He pulled her forward and bent his head toward hers. "Relax. Stop fighting me. Don't you remember how I made you feel? Don't you want to fall in love with me again?"

Before she could twist away, his mouth claimed hers, urging her lips apart. She wanted to struggle, but as she swiveled her hips, trying to free herself, her body met the hard desire of his and she found herself arching toward him, answering his needs with the clamoring demands of her own.

He released her hands and his arms went behind her back

to slowly lower her onto the thick beige carpet. His body shifted over hers and he raised his head, cupping her face between his hands. Their ragged breathing vibrated in the silent air. Linda's eyes opened into his and she moved beneath him, searching for the satisfaction only he could provide.

"Tell me you want me." His voice was husky with passion, but all the passion in the world couldn't hide his demand for her surrender.

Her body went rigid and she turned her head to the side; she didn't want to look at him. Why couldn't he have said that he loved her—needed her? Why did she always have to give in? Why did he always have to win? Couldn't their lovemaking be a source of mutual satisfaction—mutual gratification? She tried to roll away, to free herself.

"What's wrong? Can't you admit what we both know is true? Or are you too much of a puritan to accept the physical needs of your own body?" He lifted himself to look at her.

Feeling his weight shift, she moved quickly, but as she scrambled to her feet, she hit her head against the side of the washbasin. Moaning, she slid to the floor. The last thing she remembered was being caught up in Jason's arms.

Chapter Four

She awoke in bed. A cool damp cloth was folded over her forehead and warm hands were massaging her cold fingers. When she looked at Jason she immediately remembered everything that had happened.

"How are you feeling?"

"I'm all right." Her throat felt like sandpaper.

"Why did you do a crazy thing like that?"

"I told you I didn't want you touching me and I meant it." She fought to keep her voice from breaking.

He stood and circled the bed, his hands plunged deep in his pockets. "Okay. Have it your way. I won't touch you again. Not even if you beg me. Even I have feelings." He turned, and she could feel his hatred covering her like a shroud. "I'll find my satisfaction elsewhere, but what will you do, I wonder? Don't even *think* about anyone else. I'll never stand for it. I'll toss you out and get custody of Andrew so fast that you won't know what hit you. Do you understand?" His jaw grew rigid as he waited for an answer that never came. Finally he continued. "The rest of our deal stands. We're still Andrew's parents; don't ever forget that." The corner of his lip quirked in disgust. "You're such a fool." He turned and left the room.

The room wasn't cold but Linda shivered beneath the thick down quilt he had laid over her. She stared at the ceiling. Why had Jason called her a fool? Was it foolish to be upset by the way Monique had hung all over him? And that remark about him having feelings . . . what did he know about feelings? When had he ever cared about hers? So why should she worry about his?

The splashing of his shower drifted through the closed door and she was annoyed at how easily he could put her out of his mind and prepare for bed as if nothing had happened. What did she want? To fight with Jason? To be left alone? To have Jason make love to her? Suddenly she wasn't sure. If she hated him, why should she resent Monique? Was she angry only because he had humiliated her in front of his friends? Or was there more to it? Certainly she had never forgotten Jason. Did she still feel something for him besides hatred? An emotion more powerful than hatred? *That* was a possibility she was afraid to consider. She didn't want to think about it, but she was too upset to sleep and too exhausted to leave the bed. Overwhelmed by her problems, she turned toward the door separating her room from Jason's.

The sound of streaming water stopped and she listened to Jason moving around until the yellow sliver of light beneath the connecting door finally disappeared. He had gone to bed and fallen asleep, but she spent a wakeful night trying to avoid an answer she couldn't accept.

Some time during the pre-dawn hours she slipped into a fitful sleep, and when she woke she found the noonday sun flooding through the windows. It was late; Jason must have gone to work. She wondered if he'd be seeing Monique. Why should she care? It didn't matter to her. Let Monique have him. She was the type of woman he preferred anyway. She'd never let him make her cry.

Linda walked to her bathroom and turned on the shower. She wasn't going to spend any more time thinking about the two of them. She had more important things to do, like trying to find a way to fight Jason on his own terms so he couldn't keep threatening to take Andy away from her. He was the only thing that really mattered. Jason and his lady friends meant nothing to her, nothing at all.

After slipping into a pair of comfortable jeans and a tee shirt she went to check on Andy. He wasn't in the nursery, and she found him downstairs, sitting in his highchair and performing for an appreciative audience of Kim, Mrs. Smithers and Mrs. Mason. He smiled when he saw Linda and offered her his soggy teething biscuit. She sat down at the table and began playing peek-a-boo with him while Mrs. Smithers placed a cup of hot coffee in front of her.

"What would you like for breakfast?" Mrs. Smithers asked. "Although it's closer to lunch."

"Coffee and toast will be fine, thank you. We got home late last night, and I must have been more tired than I realized."

Mrs. Smithers shook her head. "It doesn't matter; Mr. Reynolds told us not to disturb you and, as you can see, Andy is no problem."

"He can nap outside this afternoon," Mrs. Mason said. "It's such a beautiful day, I can't see keeping him in." She used a washcloth to wipe Andy's hands and mouth. "What do you think?" she asked Linda.

Linda sipped the last of her coffee and rose to follow Mrs. Mason. "I think I'll join you. We can sit and talk; I've missed our little chats."

Mrs. Mason found a shady spot under a magnolia tree and settled Andy in the mesh crib Kim had set up. Linda stretched out on a lounge chair and Mrs. Mason sat across from her.

"This is a lovely home, Linda. I don't know how you ever left it." She shook her head. "And your husband . . . he loves you and Andy so much. It was such a struggle for you to do things on your own, and why?"

Linda wanted to tell Mrs. Mason that she was still struggling, that this time her problem wasn't one that money could solve. It went much deeper than that, because every time she saw Jason her emotions went to war within her. One part of her wanted to snuggle in his arms, while another reminded her that he had humiliated her and demanded retribution.

Her thoughts kept racing in circles until she was too confused to understand exactly how she felt about him. She knew she was attracted to him, Andy was proof of that, and that mutual physical attraction was strong enough to carry them through passionate moments like the one that had created Andy, but what about the other times, quiet times, when she just wanted to sit and talk? Would Jason ever be able to show any compassion, any consideration toward her? She doubted it. That was one need she had which Jason could never satisfy, yet without love she would shrivel and die.

She was thinking about this when a gray Cadillac pulled up in front of the house and Cindy Stone got out. Waving, Linda stood up and walked toward her. "Cindy, what a surprise. I didn't expect to see you today."

Cindy walked over to where Andy was napping and greeted Mrs. Mason. "I had some free time and I thought you might be interested in some lunch or shopping."

Linda's eyes moved over Cindy's neatly pressed white linen suit, then rested on her own blue jeans. "I'm not dressed for going out. I was going to spend the day lounging around the house."

"Nonsense," Cindy said. "It's time you started getting out. I know last night was a disaster." She shook her head. "That Monique is something else. You'd think she'd leave Jason alone now that he's married, but I suppose it's something you're going to have to get used to. He's a very powerful man, and a very attractive one."

Too powerful, Linda wanted to say. And too attractive. Too powerful for his own good and too attractive for mine, because he'll never know what it is to need another person. But she said nothing. Whatever she might feel about Jason, he was still her husband and she wasn't going to discuss their marital problems with anyone else.

"Well, are you coming?" Cindy asked. "Brooding around the house isn't going to solve anything."

"I suppose you're right," Linda responded. "Just give me a few minutes to change. Would you like a cool drink while you're waiting?"

"No, thanks. I'll just sit out here and enjoy the fresh air. I've been so busy with club activities and charity benefits that I haven't had much time to soak up the sun."

Linda changed into a beige raw-silk suit with a sheer, flowered chiffon blouse whose fragile fabric gave a touch of femininity to the tailored outfit. While putting her things into a brown patent-leather bag she noticed that Jason had slipped several large bills into her wallet. She was both surprised and touched. She rejoined Cindy and told Mrs. Mason that she'd be back before dinner.

While they were walking to the car Cindy turned to Linda.

"You're very lucky to have found Mrs. Mason. She's so pleasant and so fond of you and Andy. She's the perfect nanny."

Linda agreed, remembering the cold Miss Vickers. "I'm grateful for Mrs. Mason; I don't know what I would have done without her."

"Well, where would you like to go, now that you're all dressed up?" Cindy asked when they were both seated in the car.

"Anywhere. I don't know too much about the area. Why don't you just choose someplace you'd enjoy?"

"To tell you the truth," Cindy said, "I promised I'd pick up a *piñata* for my seven-year-old's birthday party, and I love Mexican food. Have you ever been to Olvera Street?"

Linda shook her head.

"It's one of the oldest streets in Los Angeles, part of the original Pueblo de Los Angeles, and it still retains its Mexican flavor. The food is delicious and they have some very interesting shops. I'm sure you'll enjoy it."

The ride to Olvera Street took them through Chinatown, and Cindy promised to take Linda there another day. She drove up several steep hills and pulled the car into a small gravel parking lot wedged between two rickety buildings. After getting a receipt from a wizened old man, Cindy guided Linda up the street and through a high picturesque arch.

The narrow courtyard was paved with brick and, since cars were prohibited, it was crowded with sightseers and shoppers. Linda felt as if she had been transported from the super-automated technology of Los Angeles to the *mercado* of a sleepy Mexican town. She sniffed the spicy aromas coming from the open stalls selling food along both sides of the street and watched an organ grinder entertain a small crowd of delighted children while his monkey walked among them with a battered tin cup. Most of the shops opened onto the sidewalk, and Linda and Cindy wandered through them all, admiring their wide variety of wares.

"They have so many different things," Linda said. "And everything is so colorful."

Cindy smiled. "It's lovely, isn't it? And it's the oldest

shopping mall in the West." She pointed to an adobe brick building. "That's the Avila House. It was built in 1818 and it's the oldest private residence in Los Angeles." She smiled. "Well, that's enough of a history lesson, now let's spend some money."

Linda purchased a small rabbit hand puppet she thought Andy would like and Cindy bought some onyx bookends that matched a chess set in her library. Linda was amazed at the huge quantities of hand-crafted leather goods and pottery. She almost bought an exquisite gray suede cape, but decided against it since she had practically no money of her own and didn't want to spend any more of Jason's than was absolutely necessary.

Finally Cindy led Linda toward a narrow adobe stairway. "Come on, I'm starving; it's about time we had lunch. I can buy my *piñata* when we've finished eating."

They opened an old glass-paned wooden door at the top of the stairway and walked into a small tile-floored vestibule. To one side was a colorfully decorated gift shop similar to the ones on the street below; on the other side was a pleasant restaurant that looked like a Mexican *cantina*. Before they went into the restaurant Cindy pointed to the crepe-paper *piñatas* hanging from the ceiling of the gift shop.

"Aren't they pretty? You fill them with candy and small party favors. Then you blindfold the children and give them a pole. You should see them scramble when the *piñata* breaks." Laughing, Cindy walked into the restaurant.

A heavy dark-haired woman in a low-necked, white draw-string blouse and multi-colored shirred skirt showed them to their table. Then a young girl, similarly dressed, asked if they wanted margaritas. Cindy held up two fingers.

The drinks were served in glasses twice the size of ordinary champagne goblets, and their saucerlike rims were coated with salt.

"Ah," Cindy said, taking a long sip. "This is the way to relax and enjoy life . . . margaritas and a leisurely lunch. Now, if only I had time for a *siesta.*"

Linda nodded in agreement while she sipped her margarita and munched fried tortilla chips dipped in *guacamole*.

They began the meal with *albondiga* soup, and Linda enjoyed its tasty little meatballs. Then she savored a mild cheese *enchilada,* which was covered with spicy red chili sauce. Refried beans and rice provided the perfect accompaniment to the *enchilada,* and they ended the meal with *flan* and Mexican hot chocolate. Linda sat back, sipping her chocolate and feeling thoroughly satisfied.

A strolling *mariachi* band came into the room and began weaving through the tables. The members were dressed in the colorful tight trousers and full-sleeved ruffled shirts of old Spain; gold-edged boleros parted to reveal thin black ties at the necks of the shirts, and hand-tooled leather boots completed their outfits. The musicians encouraged the diners to sing along with them.

Linda began singing with the other patrons, but her voice was so clear and perfectly pitched that she soon found herself singing alone, accompanied only by the guitarist and marimba player, who were now standing beside her table. Several people were staring at her, including a tall blond man two tables away. Embarrassed, she stopped singing, but everyone shouted for more, so she smiled and started singing again. When the song had finished the musicians bowed to her and the other diners applauded as Linda smiled and nodded.

"I never knew you were so talented, Linda, but that explains how you met Jason. You must have been a recording star. Am I right?"

"Not quite," Linda said. "But that was my ambition. Now, who knows?"

"What do you mean, who knows? You're good, too good to give it up. Especially now that Jason can help you."

"I'll see," Linda said. She couldn't tell Cindy that Jason would never help her with a career because a successful career would give her independence, something he didn't want her to have. "It's getting late; Mrs. Mason will be wondering where I am. Can we leave?"

"Certainly," Cindy said. "I have to be getting back myself. Ken will be home soon, and I like to have time to change for dinner." She motioned Linda away when the bill came. "This is my treat," she said, handing the waitress a charge card. "Come on. Let's get my *piñata*, then we can leave."

While Cindy tried to choose a *piñata* Linda wandered around the gift shop. She was examining a blue and white tile trivet when she felt a light tap on her shoulder and looked up to see the tall blond man who had been staring at her so intently while she was singing in the *cantina*.

"Excuse me; I didn't mean to startle you. I heard you in the restaurant, and I was impressed by your voice. Have you ever done any professional singing?"

Linda backed away and eyed him warily. She looked for Cindy and saw that her friend was busy with the sales clerk. "Not really. I'm afraid I just got carried away by the *mariachi* music. I've got to go. Please excuse me." She turned and tried to get past him to where Cindy was standing.

He put out his hand and stopped her. "Wait, please . . . you don't understand." Reaching into his wallet, he pulled out a business card and handed it to Linda. "I'm the owner of a rapidly expanding record company. We're not very big and I like to keep a handle on things, so I'm also the A and R man—you know, artist and repertoire, the guy who decides which artist should record which music, who should team up with who, and just what our company's sound is going to be. Anyway, I think your voice would be perfect for one of our new groups. Won't you at least come by for an audition?"

Linda smiled and started to walk past him. She wasn't going to make the same stupid mistake twice. Besides, she didn't have any trouble resisting this man; he didn't make her heart race like Jason did. "I think not. I've heard about these Hollywood auditions."

"No. You don't understand. This is strictly legitimate. The group I'm talking about needs a young girl singer and I think your eyes and your voice are exactly right. Won't you consider it please?"

Strictly legitimate. Ha! What did eyes have to do with singing? She shook her head and started to walk away. "I'm really not interested."

"Think it over and give me a call. I promise that all I'm interested in is your voice," he called after her.

Linda kept walking; Cindy turned as she approached.
Apparently she had been so involved in the selection of her
piñata that she hadn't heard any of Linda's conversation. She
held up a turquoise donkey and a green elephant. "Which one
do you like?"

Linda thought for a moment and absently stuffed the
business card into her pocket. "The elephant, definitely.
There's something about the way he holds his trunk that
makes him irresistible."

"The elephant it is," Cindy said. "I'm sort of partial to him
myself." She paid for her purchase and they left the shop.

"I want to thank you for a wonderful afternoon," Linda
said when they were driving home. "I really enjoyed myself."

"I'm glad. I hope we can do it again . . . often."

Linda laughed. "Sounds like a great idea. You've really
cheered me up."

"My pleasure," Cindy said. "I felt so bad about last night,
but there wasn't anything I could do. As I said, Jason is a very
powerful and attractive man, and dealing with all those
beautiful women . . . Well, you know what I mean. And
Monique's hard for any man to resist. I guess it's just
something you'll have to get used to." She turned into the
winding driveway and stopped the car at the front steps. "Oh,
darn," she said, looking at the white Mercedes parked in
front of them. "Jason's home already. I hope he wasn't
planning on having you here for an early dinner."

"Don't worry," Linda said. "And thanks again." She got
out of the car and watched Cindy drive away. So even Cindy
had noticed that Jason found Monique irresistible. But why
should *she* have to get used to anything? Why should she care
about what Jason did? But you do, a little voice reminded
her; you certainly do. She shook her head and walked into the
house. She was heading for the stairway when she heard
Jason call from the library.

He was seated behind his desk with his tie off and his collar
loosened. "Where have you been?" His deeply tanned face
was etched with tension. He leaned back in his chair, closed
his eyes and combed his fingers through his hair.

He looked so exhausted that Linda couldn't help feeling

sorry for him, and she walked over to show him the puppet she had bought for Andy. Putting it over her hand, she sidled it up to his chin. "I went to lunch with Cindy," she said, telling him about her afternoon, but leaving out the incident with the man in the gift shop. "Isn't he cute? I just couldn't resist him. Do you think Andy will like him?"

Jason smiled and grasped the hand with the puppet, pulling her down onto his lap. She hadn't planned on this; she had forgotten how easily Jason could turn a friendly conversation into a seduction scene. Immediately, she tensed and her body grew rigid. Jason lifted her chin with his thumb. "What's wrong with you? Can't you relax? I'm not going to attack you in the library."

Linda took a deep breath. "I know that, and I'm not afraid of you. But I've told you how I feel." She straightened her shoulders. "Married or not, I don't want you touching me—ever."

"I can't accept that. It's just not normal."

"Not normal or not what you want?"

"Both."

"Well, normal or not, that's how I feel. And I'm never going to change. Never."

"Never is a long time," Jason said, caressing her with his dark eyes. "I'm not known for my patience, but in this case, I think I can wait you out."

Linda remembered what Cindy had said about Jason and Monique. She slipped off his lap and walked several steps away from him. "You're so conceited. You can't believe that someone really doesn't want you. Why don't you stick to Monique and leave me alone?"

A small smile curved the edges of Jason's lips. "Monique is nice, but she's not my wife or the mother of my child. You *are*."

Linda glared at him. "An accident of fate that has nothing to do with our relationship."

Jason rose from the chair and walked toward her. He lifted a ringlet from her shoulder and twisted it around his finger. "An accident of fate . . . was that what it was, I wonder?" He released her hair and stroked his fingers down the sides of her neck. "Nothing to do with our relationship? How can you say that? Andrew is our relationship. He's our son. He's us. And you both belong to me."

"That's where you're wrong. Andy is his own person, and that's how I want him to grow up. You don't own him, and you don't own me. I won't be your punching bag."

"What do you mean, punching bag? I've never abused you."

"Not physically. But what about the names? All those horrible things you called me that first night?"

"You haven't exactly been heaping praise on me."

"Everything I've said is true."

"Because you say so?"

"I *know* so. I was there."

"So was I. Have you forgotten?"

"How could I?"

"But you'd like to."

"You know I would."

"Then we wouldn't have Andrew."

She turned away from him. "He has nothing to do with it."

"He has everything to do with it. He was conceived that night. Would you take it all back and give him up?"

"You know I wouldn't."

"Then let's declare a truce. Be my wife . . . in every sense of the word."

"And Monique?"

"She works for me."

"As what?"

He gripped her arms and his fingers bit into her flesh. "You won't even try, will you?"

"I would if I had a reason." Just give me one, she pleaded silently. Tell me you care about me as a person. Tell me you'll stop seeing Monique. Tell me the impossible. Tell me you love me.

"And I'm not reason enough?" His body tensed; she felt it through his fingers. "Making a decent home for our son isn't reason enough? Can't you see beyond your petty need for vengeance?"

She turned away. What could she say? He had made it clear

that Monique wasn't a negotiable point. He wanted them both—a meek, dutiful wife and a glamorous mistress. He hadn't changed; he wanted everything and needed nothing. Well, he wasn't going to have her. She would never give him another chance to hurt her. He could call it vengeance, but she called it self-preservation. "Let me go. You said you wouldn't touch me until I begged. Well, I'm not begging, so just let me go; I want to show Andy his puppet."

"Maybe I was upset when I made that promise. Too upset to think straight. You do have that effect on me." He sighed and dropped his hands. "Go ahead. You're too much of a child to understand anything I've said. Our discussions are pointless, so would you please leave? I want to get this finished before I change for dinner."

"A child . . . you called me that over a year ago, among other things. I haven't forgotten."

"And you don't want to."

"I have an excellent memory."

"Fine, I hope it's good company."

"I'm not complaining." She turned and walked into the hall. She had held her own with Jason. He hadn't demolished her as he had at their first meeting, so why did she feel so miserable? She leaned against the wall and waited for her body to stop shaking. What was it about Jason that made her feel, even when she won, that she had lost? She shook her head and started walking toward the kitchen. Jason was right; there were some things about him she'd never understand.

Andy was in the kitchen; he had just finished his dinner and Mrs. Mason was wiping his hands. Linda put the puppet over her hand and nestled it under his chin, tickling him lightly with her hidden finger. He laughed and Linda sat down next to him when Mrs. Mason got up. As he reached for the puppet, Linda turned to the other woman. "Why don't you have your dinner now? I'm so stuffed from lunch that I won't be wanting more than a glass of milk tonight. I'll take Andy upstairs; we'll be fine."

They went to the nursery and Linda put Andy on the shaggy rug, then stretched out beside him and began moving the puppet back and forth around him. Andy seemed to love the puppet and she kept playing with him, enjoying their time together. "Bunny," she said, flexing her fingers and making the puppet dance.

"Buh," Andy said, smiling back at her. "Buh."

"Your first word," Linda said. "You're talking!" She picked him up and ran from the room. She just had to tell someone. Andy was amazing, simply amazing.

Jason's door was open and, without thinking, she ran into the room. He was standing by his dresser, checking the contents of his wallet. His well-tailored gray evening suit clung to his muscular body and his tanned face contrasted with the pleated front of his white silk shirt. He put his wallet in his pocket, then bent his elbows and pulled his shirt cuffs out of his suit sleeves until they showed just below his wrists. Andy smiled and waved his arms, but Jason's calm demeanor made Linda feel embarrassed by her own excitement.

"That's very nice of you," Jason said, "bringing Andrew to me so I could say good night." He reached for his son.

"You shouldn't hold him. Talcum wouldn't look good on your suit."

Jason chucked Andy under the chin. "You're right. I'll have to take a raincheck. I don't have time to change. Unfortunately, I have an important business engagement this evening. It was made some time ago, but I have nothing planned for tomorrow."

"You don't have to explain. I know all about your business engagements."

Jason scowled and reached for Linda's shoulder, then looking at Andy he dropped his hands and plunged them into his pocket. "Why did you come in here? To start another argument?"

She shook her head. "No. Watch this." She put on the puppet. "Bunny," she said.

"Buh," Andy chortled. "Buh."

"Well," Jason said, smiling. "His first word." He ruffled Andy's hair. "How long do you think it'll be before he says Daddy?"

"I don't know. He could say Mommy first."

"He wouldn't dare." Jason laughed. "I won't stand for it."

"We'll see," Linda said. "I could spend all my time teaching him, then what you want won't really matter."

Jason narrowed his eyes. "You'd really do that, wouldn't you? You'd like him to hate me as much as you do, but he doesn't." He smiled at Andy and the baby reached for his necktie. "My son and I are going to be good friends, so don't waste your time trying to poison his mind against me." He kissed Andy's cheek, glanced briefly at Linda and went downstairs.

Jason's declaration reinforced Linda's belief that he didn't care about her; he only cared about his son and he would never give Andy up without a fight which, with his money and position, he'd surely win. She walked back to Andy's room, clasping him tightly to her breast as if this physical closeness could keep Jason from separating them. She sat in the rocking chair and rocked slowly back and forth until Andy dozed. Then, moving carefully so as not to wake him, she rose from the chair and placed him in the crib, gently covering him with his blanket. Walking to the window, she stared silently at the lush, landscaped grounds. Everything was quiet and deserted; Jason's spacious estate was beginning to seem more and more like a lonely prison.

She didn't realize that Mrs. Mason had returned until she heard her gathering up the toys and clothing that had been scattered around during the day. Linda bent, picked up a soft cloth ball and placed it in the toy bin. "Did you enjoy your dinner? I didn't expect you back so soon. Didn't Mrs. Smithers have time to chat?"

Mrs. Mason shook her head. "I saw Mr. Reynolds all dressed up and I thought you had to change for dinner. Aren't you going with him?"

"No, he has a business appointment. He made it while I was still living in Laguna."

Mrs. Mason's mouth opened as if she were about to say something, but she changed her mind and pursed her lips in silence as she continued adding soiled clothing to the pile of laundry. The unsaid words hung between them like a curtain of deceit, and for the first time since they had met Linda felt uncomfortable with Mrs. Mason. She dropped the cloth puppet into the toy bin and told Mrs. Mason that she was going to rest for a while, but would be available if she were needed.

She went to her room and closed the door, but she felt confined, boxed-in; she had to get out, but where could she go? Her eyes flew to the drapes billowing through the open French doors which led to the balcony. Sighing, she walked outside and stretched out on a floral-cushioned lounge chair. In her mind, Mrs. Mason's unspoken words echoed the chilling reality of her own thoughts.

Jason had looked so darkly handsome that it was hard to believe he was attending some dry business meeting. His gray evening suit was more appropriate for an elegant party than for a business conference, so it had been only normal for Mrs. Mason to think that he was going to dinner with Linda. It was true that she had told him that she didn't want to participate in his social life, but neither did she want to feel like a discarded wife. She knew that was what Mrs. Mason was thinking, and that the older woman hadn't pursued the matter because she felt that stripping away Linda's protective veil would only cause more pain.

She remembered Jason's calm acceptance of Monique's advances at the restaurant and her own silent shame when she saw the pity in everyone else's eyes. Now he had done the same thing at home; he had shown everyone how little she meant to him. It was only a matter of time before they all realized that he had no real interest in her, that she was here only because of Andy. Her mind was clouded with depressing thoughts; she hated Jason, but she wanted him to love and respect her. Could anything be more ridiculous? Taking a deep breath, she closed her eyes and let the cool evening breezes combine with the afternoon's margarita to lull her into a peaceful slumber.

The lounge's soft cushion became hard and unyielding as Linda felt herself being subjected to the roll of an unwelcome movement. Then a vibrant beat throbbed against her ear, and she snuggled closer to its comforting sound. She pressed into the taut smoothness that was cushioning her face and the grip around her tightened. An inner sense told her that she had experienced this feeling before and her eyes opened to look directly into the smoky depths of Jason's dark ones. For a minute she was still, unable to move, caught in that tranquilized limbo between sleep and wakefulness. Then the reality of the situation hit her with a deadly impact. Her body grew rigid and she struggled to get away.

His arms tightened around her like curving steel cables, pinning her helplessly against the strength of his muscular chest. "Stop acting like a child, will you? You were asleep on the balcony; I was trying to get you into bed without waking you. There's no reason to carry on like this."

Linda raised her hand and pushed it against his chest in an attempt to put some distance between them. Instead her parted fingers encountered the soft curling hairs and smooth warm skin beneath his open shirt. She blushed and pulled back as if she had touched a red-hot ember.

Jason's mouth curled in amusement. "I always take off my tie and loosen my collar when I get home. I like to feel comfortable in my own bedroom."

Linda looked around as she swung herself to the floor. She was in the master bedroom, and the huge canopied bed with its turned-down brown satin bedcovers seemed to occupy the entire room, threatening her with its impressive dominance. She wanted to back away from Jason but she was caught between him and the bed, a precarious position that made any hasty movement too dangerous to be considered.

She lowered her head and stared at the floor. Jason's beautifully buffed shoes were nearly touching her own bare toes. She spoke in a muted whisper. "I'd like to go to my own room, Jason. Please let me pass."

She watched in frozen fear as Jason's hand left his side and came up to cup her chin, raising her fearful face. His head dipped, and his lips met hers with a gentleness she hadn't known he possessed, at least not when he was dealing with her. The action was so tender and so like the comforting love that Linda had always fantasized about that her body arched into the curve of his arms to meet the firm strength of his legs and thighs. She pressed closer, molding her soft flesh to the muscular power of his.

He bent, kissing her intimately behind the ears and feathering his lips along the tender cords of her neck. Sighing, she pressed her face into his chest and inhaled, savoring the wondrous beauty of the moment, wanting it to last forever, never to end. Suddenly the mood was gone; she tensed and backed away as if she had been stung by a viper. Jason's touch might be deceptively seductive, but the fragrance that surrounded him had the relentless aura of truth. Overpowering the spicy scent of Jason's masculine cologne was the flowery sweet odor of a heavy French perfume.

Linda's heart, which only moments before had been dancing to the innocent joy of love, was now racing with the unbridled passion of anger. "How dare you kiss me while you still reek of Monique's perfume? Don't you have any sense of decency? Isn't it enough that you destroyed my life? Do you have to keep degrading me every chance you get?"

Jason gripped her shoulder when she turned to leave the room and stared at the tears welling in her hostile blue eyes. His face was contorted in anger and pain. "I was at a business meeting. We're trying to sign Monique to an exclusive film contract; you know how affectionate she is. I'm sorry if you find her perfume offensive. I don't want my outside life to affect what happens here. The next time I have a conference with her, I'll shower before kissing you. I promise." He drew her toward him once again.

Linda twisted her body, tearing herself out of his arms. "That won't be necessary. I don't want you kissing me. This was a mistake; I didn't know what I was doing. Feel free to carry on with Monique; I won't interfere. I don't have that right. I'm sure that our marriage is far more businesslike than your relationship with Monique."

Jason's attitude shifted from anger to amusement. He tilted his head, his voice was soft and condescending. "I do believe my darling wife is jealous, an interesting situation, to say the least." He lifted his eyebrows and continued to study her.

Linda bristled with anger, but she couldn't prevent a hazy red blush from covering her face. "Nothing could be further from the truth. There's absolutely no reason for me to be jealous because there's nothing emotional between us. We both know that Andy is the only reason we're together. I won't let you use me just because you struck out with Monique."

Jason relaxed into a chair. "Monique is satisfactory in every imaginable way; she never disappoints me, so don't place the blame for our problems on- her lovely white shoulders. Apparently those emotions which you consider unnecessary are impossible to avoid in our relationship. I think it's time you grew up and realized that eventually you must share a life with me." His eyes left her and drifted meaningfully toward the massive bed.

The calm assurance with which he made this remark was so overpowering that Linda shivered in the icy arrogance which cloaked the air. There was no way to answer such confident determination. He had stated the attainment of his goal as a fact which she could do nothing to forestall or avoid. He was convinced that it was only a matter of time before she would once again fall under his spell and accept his caresses as eagerly as she had on the fateful night of their first meeting. Cringing at the thought of her utter helplessness, she fled from the room before he tried to prove his statement.

Closing the door between the two rooms, she leaned against it and began sorting things out. She stiffened when she heard Jason's footsteps on the other side. Was he coming in here? No, the steps were retreating. Soon the sound of the shower told her that he was preparing for bed. Sighing, she curled up on the blue velvet window seat, still too tense to even think about sleeping. If not for Andy she would gather her few belongings and disappear, just as she had that first time. But she couldn't leave without Andy, and now that he knew about the child, Jason would never rest until he had found his son.

The shower stopped and she listened to Jason moving around his bedroom. Then the bedspring creaked, and the sliver of light under the door disappeared. Linda uncurled her legs and stood. Moonlight streamed though the French doors as she shrugged out of her clothes and into her nightgown.

Quickly, she slipped beneath the covers, drawing them up to her chin and tucking them around her body as if they could protect her from Jason's relentless power.

The house was quiet when she awakened late the next morning, and there were no sounds from Jason's room as she showered and dressed.

In the kitchen, Mrs. Mason was having coffee with Mrs. Smithers, and Andy was munching on a teething biscuit. The two women stopped chatting and smiled when they saw Linda. She poured a cup of coffee and sat down at the table, next to Andy.

Mrs. Smithers started to stand. "What would you like for breakfast?"

Linda shook her head. "I'm not hungry. This coffee will be fine."

Mrs. Smithers shook her head and busied herself at the stove. "You can't live on coffee. You fell asleep without dinner, and now you want to skip breakfast." Her calm brown eyes studied Linda's figure. "You certainly don't need to diet, so I think you'd better have something to eat."

Mrs. Mason nodded in agreement. "Andy's going to be walking before you know it, and you're going to need all your strength to keep up with him. You don't want to start fainting from hunger."

In no time at all Mrs. Smithers had prepared a large platter of bacon and eggs. Linda began eating under the motherly gaze of the two older women, and Andy reached out to grasp a hank of her hair in an attempt to get her attention. The pleasant company made her relax. In fact, she decided, she could enjoy everything about this beautiful home—if only Jason Reynolds didn't live here, too.

When she finished she offered to take Andy outside. She lifted him to her shoulders and began walking through the manicured grounds. At first it had seemed to Linda that the entire estate was one mass of green grass and shade trees, but then she realized that a clay tennis court was tucked behind a screen of avocado trees and, up above the tennis court, hidden by a circle of palm trees, was a sparkling blue swimming pool.

She knelt beside the pool and let Andy run his fingers through the water. He showed his delight with gales of laughter and Linda began splashing the water at him gently. She rose when she heard Mrs. Mason calling, and answered to indicate where she was.

"What a beautiful pool," Mrs. Mason said when she joined them and reached for Andy.

Andy was enjoying the water, and he cried when they began walking away. "It's lunchtime, young man," Mrs. Mason said. "But perhaps your mother will take you swimming after your nap. You'd like that, wouldn't you?" She hugged Andy.

"That's a good idea," Linda said. "I was wondering what I'd do this afternoon. You feed Andy, and I'll try to find a bathing suit."

Chapter Five

Once upstairs, Linda began looking through her new wardrobe for a bathing suit, but that seemed to be the one thing Miss Jenson hadn't bought. Frustrated, she checked the drawers again; there had to be something she could wear. The pool had looked so inviting, and Andy liked the water; she just wasn't going to give up her plans for this afternoon. She was all set to swim in her shorts and tee shirt when she remembered that her things from Laguna were stored in the garage; since she had practically lived at the beach last summer, she owned several bathing suits. Her only problem was that there was a row of about six garages behind the tennis court and she hadn't the slightest idea which one held her things. Sitting in her room playing guessing games wasn't going to help her, so she went downstairs to ask Mrs. Smithers.

The older woman shook her head. "Kim is the only one who knows what's in the garages, and he's driven Mr. Reynolds to work. But a bathing suit's no problem; Mr. Reynolds always keeps some on hand for guests who forget theirs. I'm sure you'll find something. Follow me." She wiped her hands and led Linda to a small guest cottage next to the swimming pool.

Linda walked in and stared at the rack of suits. "I can't believe this," she said, flipping through them.

"Mr. Reynolds has an arrangement with a swimsuit company. I think some people forget their suits just so they can come in here and get a new one. In any case, I'm sure you'll find something you like. I'll be getting back to the house, so close the door when you're finished."

The suits were arranged by size, and Linda quickly found hers. She found four bikinis that were the same style but in different fabrics and colors. She chose a white cotton one because she liked the way it contrasted with her tan. Back in her room, however, she grimaced as she studied herself in the mirror. It was scanty, covering her body's most private parts, but didn't waste any material to shield the other areas. Under ordinary circumstances she would never have had the nerve to wear something this revealing, but Jason's pool was nearly as secluded as her bathtub, so she didn't have to worry about anyone seeing her.

She took a second glance before shrugging into her short terrycloth robe. Actually, she looked pretty good in the suit. Her stomach was just as flat as it had been before her pregnancy, and her breasts and hips, while retaining their firmness, seemed fuller and more mature. She closed the robe and went into the nursery to get Andy. He was sleeping, so Linda told Mrs. Mason that she would go on ahead and wait for him at the pool.

The water looked so inviting that Linda dropped her robe on a lounge chair and dove in. It felt even more refreshing than it had looked. Although she had enjoyed Laguna Beach, the ocean waves were too rough to allow any real swimming, so she was glad for this chance to practice her strokes. She swam to the far end, pushed off, recovered the length of the pool, then pushed off again when she reached the other side. She did two laps before her breath gave out and she couldn't continue. She felt totally out of shape and vowed to practice every day until she could do better. Still panting raggedly, she climbed out of the pool, dried herself and stretched out on a lounge.

While resting on her stomach she realized that the suit's narrow straps would leave white marks that would show above the necklines of some of her dresses, so she untied them and let them hang loosely at her side; then she pillowed her head on her folded arms and closed her eyes. The sun felt so good; she sighed contentedly and let her thoughts drift aimlessly until her pleasant reverie was interrupted by a spray of cold water splattering across her back. She sat up quickly, blinking at the sunlight, and found herself looking at Jason's dripping wet thighs.

"Why did you do that?" she asked indignantly. "I was so warm and comfortable. Now I'm all wet."

"Not quite," he said perching himself on the edge of her lounge and rubbing his still damp hands across her back. He lifted a strand of hair from her shoulders and wound it slowly around his finger. "You were perspiring; I thought you'd appreciate the cool water." His eyes widened when they lowered to the soft curves of her breasts, now fully exposed by the loosened top of her bathing suit. Dropping her hair, he moved his hands to the sides of her waist. His thumbs edged higher, circling the rosy peaks.

"Stop it," she said breathlessly.

"Why?" He dipped his head, feathering his lips along the side of her neck.

Wings of ecstasy fluttered beneath his touch. She took a deep breath and closed her eyes. Her neck arched as he eliminated the distance between them. She sighed. "Umm . . ."

"That's better," he murmured. "I knew I could make you want me again."

His words blanketed her soaring desire, smothering it into nothingness. Her hands circled his wrists and pulled them off her body. "I don't want this to happen, Jason. Not now. Not ever."

"Why not? Give me one good reason."

What could she say? That she didn't trust herself with him? That she didn't want to fall in love with him again? That her hatred was the only shield she had against him, and she was still too hurt to give it up? "I can't explain, Jason, so don't ask me to. I don't want to talk about it."

"When *will* you be ready to talk about it?"

"I don't know. Don't keep badgering me." She twisted away, grasped the strings, pulled them together and retied them at the back of her neck. "What are you doing here, anyway?"

"That's a silly question. I live here, don't you remember? This is my house."

"I know it's your house. It's hard to forget, considering the way you roam around at will. You've made it quite clear that every room, including mine, is open to your explorations. I only meant that I thought you'd be working." She glanced quickly at her watch. "It's not even three o'clock."

His fingers moved lightly across her shoulder and drew delicate circles at the base of her neck. "I told you yesterday that I'd be home early today. I thought we'd spend the afternoon together—give us a chance to get to know each other."

She shrugged his hand away. "I don't want to know you any better. I know enough about you as it is, and I don't like what I know either."

He shrugged. "That's too bad, because we *are* married."

"Marriages have ended before."

"Not this one," he said, gripping her shoulders and turning her toward him. "So if that's your game, you can forget about it. You may find it hard to believe, living as we do in one of the most divorce-plagued areas of the world, but I hold my marriage vows sacred. Perhaps that's why I've never married before, and after waiting this long, I don't intend to have everything fall apart because you refuse to grow up."

Linda curled her lips and narrowed her eyes. "I'm quite grown-up, thanks to you. In fact, as you know, I'm a mother who's responsible for raising a child."

Jason nodded in agreement. "Exactly. We're both responsible for Andrew's well-being, and I intend to see that neither of us neglects that duty."

Linda glared at him in disbelief. "Are you suggesting that I would do anything to endanger Andy's welfare? How dare you?"

Jason stood and looked down at her. His hands were on his hips, and his feet were spread slightly apart, making Linda feel like a helpless ant staring up at a stone colossus. "You were negligent when you tried to hide his birth from me. That was unfair to him as well as to me; you were willing to let him suffer by depriving him of everything I could give him. But that's all over now. We're married, and Andrew is living with both his parents. That's how it is now, and that's how it's going to stay in the future. I intend to see that he has all the trappings of a normal childhood, including brothers and sisters."

Linda leapt to her feet and faced him, assuming a pose that was the mirror image of his own. "You've got to be kidding! There's no way we can ever have more children together!"

Jason's lips curled in amusement. "I thought you said you were less innocent than you used to be. Surely you know that neither of us has aged so much since Andrew's conception that we're incapable of repeating the act."

Linda shook with frustration. "I wasn't discussing the physical possibilities of the situation. I meant it was emotionally impossible."

Jason's large hand closed around her wrist and pulled her toward him until their bodies met. "On the contrary, my darling wife, I'll have no problems—either emotional or physical." His hand stroked her hip, pressing her to him and proving the truth of his statement. "And unless my intuition is very wrong," he whispered, "I don't think you will, either."

Their bathing suits were but a flimsy barrier keeping flesh from flesh, and Jason's persuasive hands moved down her back, crushing her breasts against his chest and molding her hips deeper into the firmness of his own. "Some things don't have to be discussed." His obsidian eyes studied her face, then lowered to concentrate on her softly parted lips.

She closed her eyes against the intensity of his desire, realizing that once again he was determined to make her bend to his will. She hated it. She hated him. The only thing Jason respected was power. That was why he didn't respect her; she was too weak. She had given in so easily that first night, and now he was trying to repeat that conquest. He'd never give up; the only power she had was the power to say no; and she intended to keep saying no until Jason stopped treating her like a pliable pet. But it was so hard to do, so very hard. She fought to keep her body from arching toward his.

Thick heels clumped over the brick path, and Linda and Jason sprang apart as Mrs. Mason approached with Andy in her arms. "Look who's here," Mrs. Mason cooed to the squirming child. "Your daddy's home." She gave the baby to Jason.

Linda had sprung guiltily back from Jason as soon as Mrs. Mason had arrived; a flush stained her cheeks bright red as she realized what the older woman must be thinking. Jason, on the other hand, seemed completely unperturbed. He thanked Mrs. Mason for bringing the baby out, then shifted Andy into the crook of one arm so he could take the canvas bag that she carried, containing a blanket, a bottle and several toys.

After Mrs. Mason had left, Linda watched Jason lower himself and Andy into the pool. Andy laughed and kicked his feet excitedly until Jason decided he'd had enough and handed him to Linda to be dried and changed. When Andy was comfortably settled on a blanket with a cool bottle of apple juice, Jason and Linda sat beside him on the grass.

"I'm going to have Miss Jenson arrange for swimming lessons. I doubt he'll have any problem. He takes to water like a duck."

Linda looked at Jason in surprise. "He's too young to swim; he's only nine months old. He won't be able to follow directions; he might get hurt."

"Nonsense," Jason said. "Infants have been taught to swim at that age and even younger. Their mothers usually stay in the water with them, so the children aren't afraid. He won't do the backstroke, but he'll learn to keep afloat and to reach the side of the pool. That's all I care about—his safety. With all the pools around here, swimming's an absolute necessity. You can't watch him every minute of the day, and children have an uncanny way of slipping off to where they shouldn't be. I'd like to think that falling into a pool wouldn't present any danger to Andrew . . . that he'd be able to survive until someone got to him. Those few minutes can mean the difference between life and death."

Linda shuddered at the thought of anything happening to Andy. She knew that what Jason had said was true. The newspapers constantly wrote about children being drowned in backyard swimming pools. She hadn't known that children as young as Andy could be taught to swim, but she had to agree that it was a good idea.

Andy had finished most of his bottle and thrown it to the side of his blanket. Jason retrieved it and handed it back. Linda watched with amusement as Andy laughed and flung it away again. Jason was too new at fatherhood to realize that Andy was just playing a game with him and would continue tossing his bottle and expecting Jason to fetch it, much as a child expects a puppy to fetch a stick. But Jason wasn't a puppy; he soon saw that Andy had discovered a way to manipulate his father and was exploiting his newfound power. When he realized that Andy didn't want any more juice, Jason put the bottle on the blanket and picked up the giggling baby, holding Andy's soft cheek near his own.

Linda watched them grinning at each other. Their features were so similar that, looking at Andy, she felt she knew exactly how Jason had looked as a child. Even if she had never met Jason again she would have seen him every time she looked at Andy. There was no denying that he was Andy's father, and there was no doubting his love for the child.

"He does look like you," she said, speaking without realizing what she was saying. Almost before the words left her lips she wanted to swallow them back.

"Of course he looks like me," Jason said. "Why shouldn't he? He's my son, isn't he? You're not trying to deny that, are you?"

"Of course he's your son. I never said he wasn't. I only wish . . ."

"You only wish what? That he *wasn't* my son? That you didn't have to share him with me? That you could have him all to yourself again?"

Linda turned away, bitter tears welling in her eyes. Yes, she thought, I wish I could take him away. I wish I could make you suffer the way I've suffered. I want you to know the misery of loving someone who doesn't love you. All these vengeful wishes raced through her mind, but she closed her eyes and said nothing.

As if he had read her thoughts, Jason turned and looked at her, unforgiving hatred darting from his eyes. "When I think of what you tried to take from me, I could strangle you. Just be grateful that you didn't cheat me of more than nine months of watching Andrew grow. And you can forget any ideas about getting a separation from me and taking him away with you. I'll never give him up." He turned and strode quickly toward the house, still carrying Andy, who never even tried to look back at her.

Linda walked to the pool and dipped her fingers in the cool water. She shivered as she recalled the loathing she had seen in Jason's eyes—so different from the love they radiated toward his son and from the emotion she had once, though it felt like another life to her now, hoped he would feel for her. She had heard of women being trapped in loveless marriages for the sake of their children, but had never thought it would happen to her. She knew Jason meant what he said about keeping Andy. If she took him away Jason would only find her again; he would hire the best lawyers, and there was no way she could fight him and win. It was a horrible thought, but the child she loved was the instrument Jason would use to keep her in a situation that threatened to destroy her.

She straightened and headed back to the house, after gathering up Andy's things and the soiled towels, dropping the latter in the laundry room at the back of the house, then trudging up the stairway. Jason had taken Andy to the nursery, where Mrs. Mason was bathing him. When she closed the door to her room, she heard the hiss of Jason's shower, but she felt too depressed to change so she tightened the belt on her terrycloth robe and stretched out on a lounge outside her room.

Her problem had no solution; she didn't even want to think about it. Why bother? She would only get more depressed. She took a deep breath, made her mind go blank and stared morosely at the swaying palms beneath the balcony. She tensed when the door of the adjoining room opened and Jason called her. She thought about not answering; maybe he would go away, but that was wishful, not wise, thinking. Jason would eventually find her, and when he did he would only be angrier. "I'm out here, Jason, on the balcony." She gritted her teeth in preparation for the battle that was sure to come.

His dark hair was still damp from his shower and it glistened softly above his aquiline features. He had changed into a charcoal gray evening suit and was fastening his gold wristwatch as he spoke to her. "What are you doing out here? Why aren't you dressing for dinner?"

Linda fought back the urge to tell him to get out of her room, that she would change when *she* felt like it. "I'm resting; I don't plan on dressing for dinner. I'm not hungry. I'll probably have some milk and cookies before I go to bed."

Jason glared at her. "I told you I was sorry about having to leave you yesterday, and I said we would spend tonight together. I thought you'd be dressed by now. This isn't your little beach colony; we don't wander around in bathing suits. Now, will you please get ready? We're going to be late as it is."

Linda didn't move, but she couldn't suppress her feelings any longer. "How was I supposed to know that you were serious about having dinner with me tonight? You mentioned it so casually, and we never made any definite arrangements. I thought you were just trying to soothe your conscience for being out with Monique last night. If that's your reason, don't bother. I couldn't care less about who you spend your time with as long as it isn't me. It's pointless to wine and dine me, because it won't change how I feel. I know what you are, and you'll never deceive me again, so don't waste your charm on me. And, as for my friends in Laguna Beach, they're a lot more decent in their bathing suits than Monique is in those low-cut gowns which leave nothing to the imagination . . . not that you need to imagine."

Jason was at her side in one violent movement. His hands went beneath her arms and lifted her out of the chair. "You are my wife. I assumed that it would be natural for us to dine together. I didn't think I'd have to make an appointment. We're beyond the dating stage, you know . . . or perhaps you don't know? Just because I've allowed you to keep me out of your bed, don't think I'm going to put up with every little bit

of nonsense you decide to dish out. And don't think you're
going to provoke me into giving you grounds for divorce and
a way to get custody of Andrew, either. No matter what you
think of my morals, I won't let you take my son from me. You
tried that for nine months, and you'll never do it again, not
ever. As for Monique, she has more warmth and kindness in
one little finger than you have in that entire virginal body of
yours."

"You of all people should know that I'm not a virgin."

"Why . . . because you had my son? Do you think that
makes you a warm, mature woman, capable of loving and
satisfying a man? That just shows how naïve you are. Your
heart is encased in ice, and you're too warped by imaginary
grievances to provide your child with a proper home and
family. But I'm equally determined to see that you don't
destroy his life. You can make yourself as miserable as you
want, but if you ever do anything to hurt Andrew I'll make
you wish you'd never been born." He released her and let her
sink back on the lounge. "Forget about tonight. Go ahead
and stay home and brood about the way I've ruined your
life—but you're not going to ruin mine, and you're not going
to ruin Andrew's."

Linda looked away from him and listened to the door slam.
Didn't he know that she already wished she'd never been
born? All their discussions ended in an argument, but that
was understandable: She hated him, and he saw her only as
Andy's mother. All he wanted from her was more children
who would look like him, think like him, be extensions of
him. Living symbols of his power, that's what he wanted; he
never mentioned love because love never entered his
thoughts.

But love existed, and her love for Andy would make her
stay with Jason. But nothing would make her let Jason use her
body again. No amount of verbal abuse or cajoling would
make her change her mind. First he had made her a recepta-
cle for his lust and now he wanted a personal baby-making
machine. He never thought of her as a person—a woman who
needed love and understanding—and he never would. Jason
was too set in his ways, but she would never let him humiliate

her again; their problems wouldn't disappear, and time would only increase the tension between them. She wondered what would happen when Andy got old enough to realize how strained their relationship was. They'd never be able to convince him, or anyone else, that they had anything even close to a normal marriage.

Sighing disconsolately, she rose and went inside. She was still tired, but she couldn't stay in her bathing suit anymore. Jason's remark about her friends had made her feel slovenly, and she tried to soothe her shattered ego by letting a warm shower flow over her body. She heard Jason drive away as she stood by the closet trying to decide on an outfit, but there was no longer any point in getting dressed for dinner because Jason really had gone without her.

Well, she might as well be comfortable, she decided, and slipped into a long white cotton gown with no zipper or buttons. The elasticized neckline, sleeves and waistline expanded when she pulled down the dress and smoothed the long delicately gathered skirt until it flowed fluidly over her hips. The outfit was comfortable, yet soft and feminine, and once again she was grateful for Miss Jenson's good taste. She brushed her hair loosely over her shoulders and was about to go down to the kitchen for a sandwich and milk when she heard a knock at the door.

"Come in."

Kim stood in the doorway, holding a large silver tray loaded down with dishes. "Mr. Reynolds said you weren't feeling well and told Mrs. Smithers to have me bring this tray to your room." He set the tray on a chest while he spread a linen cloth on the small round table in front of the window. Then he took the dishes off the tray and put them on the table. "Enjoy your dinner. I'll come for the dishes when you're finished." He picked up the tray and left the room.

When the door had closed behind him, Linda walked to the table. She had told Jason that she wasn't hungry and would be having only a glass of milk for dinner, yet he had asked Mrs. Smithers to prepare an entire meal for her. Why? Why should he care about what she ate? He didn't really care about her, did he? She eyed the small baby shrimp lying on a crisp bed of lettuce. She hadn't felt like eating, but one taste of the shrimp as they mixed with the spicy cocktail sauce on her tray left her hungry for the rest. They whetted her appetite for the two charbroiled lamb chops, small roasted potatoes and nest of broccoli that were on a larger plate. She had one cup of coffee with a bowl of homemade peach cobbler and took her second cup to the terrace.

A full moon hung over the palm trees; the scene looked more like a South Sea island than Beverly Hills. Linda walked to the edge of the balcony and rested her coffee cup on the railing. It was a night made for romance, and she didn't doubt that Jason was using it for just that purpose. She knew that he wasn't wasting any time pining over her, yet much as she claimed to hate him she couldn't stop thinking about him. Well, she wouldn't do it anymore. She would stop right now; keeping busy was the answer. Putting all thoughts of him from her mind, she decided to clear the dishes and return them to the kitchen herself, but she noticed that Kim had taken the tray, so she would have to bring one up.

On her way down to the kitchen she opened Andy's door and saw that his room was dark. Mrs. Mason had probably just put him to bed, so she decided not to go in; if he wasn't in a deep sleep she might wake him, and then it would be difficult to get him back to sleep again.

Mrs. Smithers was talking to Kim when Linda came into the kitchen. "I'm sorry to bother you, but I need a tray for the dishes."

Kim frowned. "I'll get them. You should have buzzed me on the intercom when you were finished. Mr. Reynolds wouldn't want you walking around when you're not feeling well."

"I feel much better, Kim, and I'm perfectly capable of bringing my own dishes downstairs. I'm not used to being a lady of leisure; I used to be a working girl, you know."

"But you're not a working girl anymore, Mrs. Reynolds, and Mr. Reynolds pays me to do these chores. You wouldn't want me to lose my job, would you?" Kim smiled as he picked up the tray.

"No, of course not, Kim. I never thought of that." Linda

walked to the sink where Mrs. Smithers was loading the last dishes into the dishwasher. "I want to thank you for the delicious dinner. I didn't realize how hungry I was. I enjoyed everything."

"I'm glad you did. Mr. Reynolds told me to be sure you had a good dinner. He said you weren't feeling well and wanted to go to bed with just a glass of milk, but he felt you would hurt yourself more by not eating. As usual, he was right."

"Did Mr. Reynolds say where he was going?"

Mrs. Smithers frowned. "No, although he mentioned dinner reservations and seemed upset that you weren't able to go with him." She closed the dishwasher and wiped her hands. "Well, that takes care of that; I think I'll relax in my room . . . unless you need me?"

"No," Linda said. "I'm going to curl up with a good book. I'll be in the library."

The library walls were made of thick walnut paneling, covered by floor-to-ceiling bookshelves. The huge brick fireplace had been cleared of ashes and logs, and masses of potted green plants sprouted from the firebox. All the chairs and sofas were covered in tan leather, and Jason's desk and credenza matched the dark walnut on the walls.

Linda stood in the doorway and admired the masculine simplicity of the room. It was clearly a man's retreat, yet without Jason it looked restful and inviting to her. She walked along the walls, scanning the books on the shelves. Many were valuable leather-bound first editions, and these were kept behind glass doors. One complete section was filled with books detailing the history of the entertainment industry, records and movies in particular. There were also copies of many current best-sellers. Linda wanted something to distract her from her own problems, so she decided to go for an interesting novel.

After selecting several, she took them over to the desk, where the light was good, to thumb through them. As she relaxed in the high-backed swivel chair she glanced down and saw Jason's house keys lying on the desk next to a pile of unopened mail. Beside them were several thickly bound typewritten manuscripts. Setting her books aside, she began leafing through one of the manuscripts and was surprised to find that it was a script proposal, an adaptation of a recent critically acclaimed novel. She had never seen a film script before and was intrigued by the quick pacing and snappy dialogue.

After returning the books to the shelves, she stretched out on the sofa to read the script. It was as gripping as the novel itself had been, and she didn't stop reading until she heard Jason's car coming up the drive. She remembered the keys lying on the desk; if they were Jason's personal set he'd probably ring the doorbell to get in. Since she was already up it was pointless to disturb anyone else. Closing the script but keeping a finger in her place, she stood and padded barefoot to the door.

Jason was starting up the steps when she opened the door. He smiled in apparent friendliness. "Well, this is a pleasant surprise."

When he reached the terrace, where she was standing, he smiled and rested his arms on the wall she was leaning against, imprisoning her between them. "You waited up for me." His hands dropped, framing her cheeks.

She shook her head and tried to speak, but her mouth had gone dry. Still looking up at him, she ran her tongue over her lips. After all this time Jason's eyes could still turn her insides into a swarm of butterflies. His hands shifted, drawing her face toward his. His lips moved softly over hers, urging them apart, and the tip of his tongue pressed forward passionately, seeking to mate with hers. She felt herself drowning in the ocean of his caress and made one last desperate effort to twist away. She didn't want this. She didn't want to give in, to lose control. She didn't want Jason to win—not again, not this time. But he held her firmly, intensifying his kiss, probing the depths of her mouth, stroking her cheeks and her neck, setting a fire that consumed her protests and burned away the flimsy barrier of her resistance. Unable to fight any longer, she dropped the script and put her arms around his neck.

"Ouch." Jason released her and bent to rub his hand over his instep. "What's this?" he asked, picking up the script. "I thought you were kicking me." He looked at the cover, then straightened his body. "Where did you get this?"

"I found it in the library. I was looking for something to read and I saw this on the desk. I didn't expect you home this early."

Jason closed the door and led Linda back to the library. He walked to the desk and returned the script to the pile. "You mean that you came in here to snoop because you thought you wouldn't be discovered?"

"I didn't mean that at all. Must you twist everything I say just so you can scream at me? I wasn't spying on you. Why would I do that? I saw the script on your desk and I wanted to read it. I had no idea your library was off-limits to me. After all, we are married—as you never tire of telling me."

Jason looked at her with languid amusement. "There's no need to remind *me* of our marital vows. I've always been willing to keep them . . . every one of them. You're the one who's been neglecting your wifely duties."

Linda put her hands on her hips and glared at Jason. Her breasts strained the bodice of her dress, and her breath came in vehement spurts. "Damn you, Jason Reynolds. You know exactly what I'm talking about, don't you? But you just can't stop twisting everything I say. You love making me feel like a fool. How dare you talk about vows . . . duties . . . ? What about honoring, cherishing, remaining faithful?" She turned away, fighting back tears of both anger and misery.

"Making you feel like a fool? Did you ever think about how I felt tonight . . . having to make excuses about where you were?" Jason's lips tautened. He shook his head. "No, of course you didn't. You were too busy thinking about yourself."

"Stop it, do you hear me, stop it!" Even in her upset state she knew that Jason had a point, but she didn't want to think about him that way—to hear his side—to let down her guard. She didn't want to become vulnerable, not again. This time she wanted to do the hurting, to hurt him the way he had hurt her. Turning back to him, she lifted her hands and pounded her fists against his chest.

He caught them and drew her to him. "Okay, it's over; you've had your say. Now, stop it, or you'll have the whole house down here." He pressed her head against his chest and ran his fingers through her hair.

Linda closed her eyes, but she couldn't hold back her tears. She sobbed soundlessly while Jason lifted her and carried her to the sofa. He held her in his lap and his soothing hands moved over her body. It felt so good, so right—it always had. She loved being in Jason's arms, loved his touch. That was why she had let him make love to her—that was why Andy had been born. It had been her fault as well as Jason's, and she couldn't keep blaming him, but she couldn't stop either. She was still too hurt to think about being fair.

"It's all right, Jason. I'm better now." Reaching up, she wiped her eyes with her fingers. "Forget it."

"Here, let me." Jason cupped her chin and dabbed his handkerchief across her cheeks.

She watched him silently.

"I can't forget how good you felt." Dropping the handkerchief, he ran his hands down her arms and over her breasts.

His words reminded her of how *she* had felt. But while he was thinking of physical responses, she was remembering the emotional ones, how confused and hurt she had been when he had started screaming at her, calling her names. She had loved him that first night—she knew that now. And in her own naïve stupidity she had thought he loved her. But she had been wrong—so wrong. She had been too inexperienced to know that a man like Jason could make love without being in love.

He nibbled and teased her earlobe as his hand moved down her body, curved over her hip and followed the long line of her legs down to the hem of her dress. For a few tantalizing minutes he stroked her ankle, then his hand slipped under her dress, caressed her leg and began gliding higher.

Her flesh flowered beneath his touch, but her pride was like an aphid, eating away at the blossom of her love. She couldn't let Jason make love to her; he didn't care about her. He was using her again, trying to bring her under his power; he knew her body was the weakest link in her chain of resistance.

She forced herself to move; better the deprived misery she was feeling now than the hopeless rejection that would follow Jason's lovemaking. She shifted out of his arms and got to her feet again.

"What happened?" Jason was at her side, holding her arm, staring into her eyes.

"Nothing's happened," Linda said. "And nothing's going to." She took a deep breath. "I'm going to bed now . . . alone."

Jason stepped back. For a minute, the muscle in his jaw throbbed angrily, then he leaned against the walnut desk and relaxed. "You're still not ready to grow up."

"I'm as grown-up as I want to be."

"But not grown-up enough to be my wife?"

"Not even when I'm old and gray."

Sighing, Jason slid into the chair behind the desk. "Well, in that case, would you mind leaving? I've wasted enough time on you for one night. I might as well do some work; it's about the only thing I'm going to accomplish this evening." He reached for a stack of paper. "Good night, my little icicle." He picked up a pen and began writing.

Linda ran upstairs and into her bedroom, where she paced nervously, too agitated to sleep. Why did she keep letting Jason do this to her? He treated her like a misbehaving child and refused to see her as a grown woman. He thought she was a piece of property, to be used whenever the whim struck him. Never once did he mention mutual love, only wifely duty. Well, he could forget that; she would never be a real wife. That would only give him more power than he already had.

Her first experience with Jason's lovemaking had been bad enough. It had taught her that the sensuous pleasures of his touch had to be paid for with the bitter tirade which followed. She couldn't afford to let it happen again; her pride wouldn't allow it. Jason had hurt her, and she wasn't going to let him forget it, not even if she had to spend the rest of her life reminding him. She walked out on the balcony and clutched her arms around her to ward off the chilling night air. No matter how warm it had been during the day, the temperature always dropped once the sun went down, because there was little humidity in Southern California and gentle Pacific breezes cooled the evenings.

Her hand curved over the wrought-iron railing as she looked out over the lawn. She had to find a way to show Jason that she wasn't as helpless as he thought she was. She had to show him that she was a mature woman, able to take care of her own needs as well as Andy's. Once he realized that she wasn't such easy prey maybe he would respect her and leave her alone.

The light was still on in the library. She could see an illuminated patch glistening on the carefully tended lawn. She found it even more annoying to think she had to endure another evening of mental torture while Jason was free to do his work; work that would add to the exorbitant income which would guarantee him custody of Andy, despite all her protests. Money—that was the answer, the only answer Jason would understand. If there was just some way she could earn enough money to give Andy a decent home maybe she could convince a court to release her from this ridiculous marriage and grant her custody of her son.

Her frantic pacing came to an abrupt halt. Snapping her fingers in triumph she ran back into her bedroom and walked directly to the closet. She searched through the pockets of her beige silk suit until she found the business card the man at the Mexican restaurant had given her. He had said the offer was entirely legitimate. Maybe it was. Maybe there were some people in Hollywood who really were interested in discovering talent that couldn't be judged in a bedroom.

She looked at the card. *Steven Douglas, President, Karizma Recording Studios.* She thought for a minute; she had heard about Karizma Studios when she lived in Laguna Beach. A lot of new songwriters and folk singers had gotten their start by recording for Karizma, and they spoke highly of the professional nature and artistic ability of the company's executive management. Well, Linda thought, it's worth a try.

I'll call tomorrow and insist on a daytime audition at the studio. That should show I mean business.

As she closed the balcony doors she glanced down and saw that the light from the library continued to reflect on the silent lawn. Still fuming as she remembered Jason's condescending treatment, she latched her door and prepared for bed.

Chapter Six

Linda stopped at the glass-enclosed kiosk and gave her name to the parking attendant. He checked his clipboard, then raised the gate to let her through. She parked the station wagon in the spot he indicated and got out, leaving the keys in the ignition. It took a moment to smooth the skirt of her blue silk shirtwaist and adjust the decorative chains of varying lengths that glistened beneath its simple collar. As she pushed her hair back from her face the plain gold band on her left hand caught a sunbeam, reminding her of Jason and her marriage. If this job was going to start her on a new life without Jason, she might as well take the first step now. Jason would never be a real husband to her, so there was no point in wearing his ring. Hesitating for only a moment, she slipped it off her finger and dropped it into her small beige leather clutch purse. Trying to convince herself that she was doing the right thing, she straightened her shoulders and held her head high as she walked toward the squat glass-and-concrete building.

Huge bronze letters and a gigantic replica of a record disc dominated the roofline, proclaiming it the home of Karizma Records. Linda walked through the electronically controlled glass doors and was greeted by the welcome chill of air conditioning. When she told the elevator operator that she wanted to see Mr. Douglas he nodded and pushed the button labeled *Executive Offices*. The elevator rose, then stopped; Linda stepped onto a deep rust-colored carpet and spoke to the attractive young receptionist.

"I have an appointment to see Mr. Douglas."

"Your name, please?"

"Linda Brown," she said, glancing at her unadorned left hand.

She had called Steven Douglas at ten o'clock that morning, identifying herself as the girl from Olvera Street. When the secretary said that he would see her and asked for her name, she had given her maiden name. Jason was so well-known in Hollywood that she didn't want to risk being asked if she was related to him. She couldn't let him know anything about her new career—at least, not until she was certain of its success.

She had told Miss Jenson that she was going shopping and had asked to borrow the car. When Miss Jenson had checked with Jason, he had suggested that she let Kim drive her, but Linda had insisted that she would be more comfortable driving herself, and Jason finally consented. She had no intention of letting Kim drive her so he could report back to Jason, because once Jason found out he would definitely put an end to her plans. She knew he wouldn't let her do anything that might make her independent and give her the financial ability to fight him for custody of Andy.

After checking a list on her desk the receptionist told Linda to go through the first glass door on the left, which said, in gold lettering, *Office of The President.*

A middle-aged, carefully groomed secretary rose from her desk and came toward Linda. "How do you do, Miss Brown? Mr. Douglas is expecting you; I'll take you right in." She rapped lightly on a door marked private, then opened it and stepped aside to let Linda pass in front of her.

Steven Douglas came from behind his desk and held out his hand. "Linda, I'm so glad you decided to come." He motioned her to a white sectional sofa facing the floor-to-ceiling glass wall, seated himself in a comfortable club chair opposite her, lifted a tray of cigarettes from the circular cocktail table which separated them and offered her one. When she refused he asked about coffee or a cold drink. Again she shook her head. "Very well, Linda," he said, "let's get down to business. You have a fine singing voice. Have you ever done any recording?"

"No."

He lifted one tawny brow in surprise. "Then, I suppose

we'd better begin at the beginning. You know, of course, that you have an excellent ear for pitch, and your voice has a soft, soothing quality. I noticed that when you were singing with the *mariachi* band, but that's all I know about you. Why don't you tell me something about yourself? Even if you've never done any professional singing, surely you've had some voice training?"

"Actually, the only training I've had was from the choirmaster of our church in Kansas. I've also done some singing on my own, but I haven't been too successful financially."

Steven Douglas nodded in agreement. "The streets of Hollywood are filled with aspiring actors and singers from every small town in the country. They park outside my door holding tapes and discs they want me to listen to. They come here looking for stardom, but most of them end up haunting the unemployment office, rarely earning more than two thousand dollars a year. Though you may not believe it, considering the way we met, my biggest job is avoiding talent, not discovering it. However, I think this is your lucky day. I have a small group that's been recording with me. They're good, but I think they need a female lead with just your type of voice. They're downstairs cutting a record right now. Would you like to meet them?"

Linda nodded and Steve rose, motioning for her to precede him to the door. He told his secretary that he would be downstairs in the recording studio if he was needed for anything critical, but short of an emergency he asked not to be disturbed.

The entrance to the recording studio was even more closely guarded than the entrance to the executive offices had been, and Linda was given a plastic visitor identification card to attach to her collar before being permitted beyond the vestibule into the hushed atmosphere of the soundproof booth. Signs warning that a recording was in session and asking for silence flashed their red electronic message from every wall. Steve motioned Linda to an empty chair, then settled himself in the one next to hers.

Linda leaned forward and watched the technicians in the booth adjust dials until they got the effect they wanted from the music being played by a trio of bearded young men in the studio below. Midway through the song, the guitarist missed a beat, shook his head, removed his earphones and asked for a break. The machines stopped grinding and the technicians left their seats and began stretching. Immediately the atmosphere became more relaxed.

Steve stood and turned to Linda. "Come on, I want you to meet the group." He led her out of the glass booth and onto the floor of the recording studio, where the trio was relaxing with cool drinks.

"Boys, I want you to meet Linda Brown. She's the singer I mentioned. Linda, meet Jeff, Terry and Bill, otherwise known as the Sapphires. They took that name because they all have blue eyes; that's a requirement I may have forgotten to mention."

He hadn't forgotten, but she had certainly misunderstood. Linda smiled as the Sapphires' six blue eyes stared straight into hers. Grinning self-consciously, she turned her head away.

Jeff clapped his hand to his thigh. "Eyes match. That's okay. Now, let's hear her sing. Do you know the words to *It's Such a Lonely Night?*"

Linda nodded. The group took up their instruments and crowded around her. They began singing as they played, and Jeff motioned for her to join in. Linda sang softly at first so as not to dominate the male voices, then, as always, she became lost in the music and her voice rose, filling the air with its clear, melodic tones. The men lowered their voices and muted the tones of their instruments. In the booth movement ceased and conversations halted as all eyes turned to the microphone where Linda was standing. When she had finished she was rewarded by an outburst of applause from the Sapphires as well as the recording technicians. Then before she had a chance to say anything, Linda listened to her voice streaming from the speakers at the sides of the studio.

"I told them to record you," Steve said. "Now we know what you'd sound like on a disc." He turned to the Sapphires. "What do you think, boys? Isn't she good?"

The men nodded. "She's perfect," Bill said. "Just what we need, blue eyes and all."

"Great," Steve said. "Why don't we go to my office and talk contract?"

Linda couldn't believe that the group wanted her after hearing only one song, but she said yes before they could change their minds. She told them that she didn't have an agent and was willing to accept a smaller percentage of the group's future earnings than the men were receiving. She felt this was only fair since they had worked so much harder during the formation of the group.

"Super," Jeff said, shaking her hand. "Can you be here tomorrow for a recording session at ten o'clock?"

Linda thought for a moment. Jason had said he wanted her to get out to meet people and do some shopping, so she could probably think up some excuses for being away from home. She knew she would miss Andy, but she realized Mrs. Mason would take good care of him, and anyway she was doing this for him, wasn't she? "I'm sure I can. I can't tell you how grateful I am."

"This arrangement is going to make us all rich," Steve said as he walked Linda to the door. "Be sure to give your address and phone number to my secretary before you leave."

Linda tugged at her bottom lip. "I can't do that, Mr. Douglas. If anything comes up, I'll call you."

"Call me Steve. I've been calling you Linda all morning." He looked at her and frowned. "We need your phone number in case we have to reach you. It's kept in the office; we never give it out."

"I'm sorry, Steve, but that's the way it has to be. I'm living in temporary quarters right now, and I don't want to give out the address or phone number. If I earn enough money from these recordings I'll be able to move and get things straightened out. Then there won't be any problem."

Steve shook his head as he walked her to the elevator. "It's an unusual arrangement, but it won't last long. You're going to be rich soon. Do you need an advance?"

Linda could tell he was wondering about her expensive

clothing, but she wasn't going to satisfy his curiosity. She couldn't chance Jason's learning about this until she was sure of the results. "Thanks, but I'll be fine." She shook his hand and thanked him again when the elevator arrived. Checking her watch she realized that she had been here longer than she expected and wouldn't get home before late afternoon. She hoped no one would ask too many questions about where she had spent the day.

The sun had been beating down on the car during the entire time she was in the building, and Linda felt as if she were entering a blast furnace when she seated herself behind the wheel. She turned on the air conditioning, but it blew hot air and didn't cool the car at all, so by the time she pulled up to the house her silk dress was clinging to the seat of the car and her face was damp with perspiration. She felt completely drained and sticky.

She parked, slipped her wedding band back onto her finger to avoid questions and went up to her room, stepping out of her rumpled clothing as soon as she had shut the door. Then she stood under a cool shower and washed her hair as well as her body. After patting herself dry, she dressed in a full-length, pale-pink, halter-necked dress with white eyelet edging that gave a modest appearance to a plunging neckline that might otherwise have been very daring. The white sandals that completed her outfit were barely visible under the dress's flowing skirt.

Her hair was still damp, but she was too hot to use a blow-dryer, so she ran a comb through it and let it dry into a long halo of naturally curling ringlets. Feeling refreshed and satisfied with her appearance she went looking for Andy. He wasn't in his room, so she went downstairs, thinking he might be eating, but the kitchen was deserted. Even Mrs. Smithers was nowhere to be seen. Her stomach growled, reminding her that she had missed lunch, so she took a tray of cold milk and miniature Danish pastries out to the patio by the breakfast room and settled herself on a comfortable lounger.

She dozed on and off and was still sitting there when Jason drove up and waved to her.

He took the steps two at a time. "Where were you?" he asked. "I called twice, and you were out both times."

"I did some shopping." She hated to lie, but it was the easiest answer.

"Did you buy that today?" Jason asked, indicating the outfit she was wearing.

"No, Miss Jenson bought me this. In fact, she bought me so much that I really didn't need anything. I just wanted to do some window shopping."

Jason's brows lifted doubtfully. "You mean you spent the whole day shopping and didn't buy anything? That's hard to believe. Ken says Cindy can spend a week's earnings in just a few hours."

Linda's guilty conscience made her especially sensitive to Jason's questioning. "Well, I'm not Cindy. You should be happy that I didn't squander your money instead of giving me the third degree."

Jason held his hands out. "Hold on . . . don't snap my head off. I'm not looking for a fight, just conversation." He held up two fingers on each hand. "Peace."

Linda smiled. "Peace. . . . I'm sorry, Jason, I guess I'm being grouchy. I'm just tired. How was your day?"

"The usual nonsense. My stockholders expect a business operation based on profits and losses, but they forget that our product involves dealing with a horde of temperamental stars."

"Come on, Jason, recording stars aren't temperamental. They just want to make sure they sound right when the public hears them. You know how fickle fans are; one bad recording and you're off the charts."

Jason pursed his lips and nodded. "I suppose you're right. Recording stars are bad enough, but now that JMR Industries has started making movies . . . whew! They're mainly for television, but now we're branching into the theaters. That's why Monique is so important to us. She has a good following, and all her movies are box-office hits."

Linda stiffened at the mention of Monique's name; she remembered what Cindy had said about Monique being hard to resist. "You don't have to explain your relationship with Monique. It doesn't concern me. You're free to do as you please, in your social life as well as your business life."

Jason frowned. "Well, well, it seems I'm doubly blessed. My wife goes shopping without spending my money and she doesn't care if I have an affair with a very attractive movie star. I wonder what I did to deserve all this."

Linda raised her eyes to meet his. "Would it matter if I did care?" she asked softly.

Jason's eyes touched hers. "It might. After all, you are my wife, the mother of my child. I imagine that you could demand a certain degree of fidelity on my part. I expect no less of you."

Linda lowered her gaze and reflected on his statements. Nothing had changed. True, he wasn't ridiculing or baiting her, but he still hadn't mentioned love. He only wanted her around because she was Andy's mother. If not for Andy, she wouldn't be here and he wouldn't be calling her his wife. "You have no reason to doubt my fidelity, despite what our first meeting may have led you to believe."

Jason moved as stealthily as a stalking leopard, and Linda wasn't aware of his approach until she raised her eyes. He shifted her legs away from the edge of the lounge and lowered himself to the seat beside her. Then he took both her delicate hands in his large masculine one. His other hand cupped her chin, lifting her face to his. "What are you trying to tell me? That what happened that night wouldn't have happened if I were just any man? Are you saying that I'm special? That you want me as much as I want you?"

The turbulent depths of his dark brown eyes swirled into clarity and Linda could see the raging desire rise potently to the surface, ravishing her body with his seductive cravings. He would never understand that what she had felt for him that night was much stronger than mere desire; even though they had just met, she had loved him, just as she had loved Andy at first sight, a different kind of love, but equally intense.

The thought made her withdraw in fright. Was it possible that she loved Andy, not only for himself, not only because he was her child, but also because he was Jason's child? Did she still feel for Jason what she had felt that first night—maybe even more, now that they shared Andy?

Andy and Jason. Jason and Andy. Their facial features were so similar that it would be impossible to love the child without loving the father whom he so strikingly resembled. Her pride recoiled at this realization, but her heart insisted on its truth. She still loved Jason—in spite of everything or because of everything, what did it matter? She still loved him, but she could never admit that to him; he'd never understand. He'd only laugh, call her a foolish child, then take that love and use it against her. She couldn't allow that. Maybe if she became a successful recording star, maybe then he would see her differently, as a talented woman—like Monique?

That was what she really wanted, his respect *and* his love, but she could never hope for either until he stopped issuing orders and treating her like an inferior. Oh, she was being pampered, that was true; he had bought her expensive clothes and given her a spacious home, but what good was all that? A prison was a prison even if the bars were made of gold. No, she could never risk telling Jason of her feelings for him until his attitude toward her had changed.

"No, Jason, I don't want you or anyone else. All I'm saying is that you don't have to worry about my fidelity."

Desire hovered in his eyes, then changed to anger. "So you don't care if I have an affair with Monique, because that lets you off the hook? It doesn't matter who I sleep with so long as it isn't you?"

The hands which had gently caressed hers only minutes before became painful pincers biting into her flesh. Frightened by the savage hatred in the depths of his eyes, she tried to break free but her efforts were futile; his fingers were like tempered steel.

"Dinner is ready whenever you are," Kim said from the doorway.

Jason stood, ran his fingers through his hair, then offered Linda his hand. "Come on, we might as well go in to dinner before our discussion ruins what little appetite I have."

They ate in the dining room and Linda welcomed the

distance that the long oak table put between them. Any attempt at conversation seemed pointless, so they ate in silence. Mrs. Smithers was an excellent cook, and the meal was perfect, from the chilled tomato aspic and the chicken Marengo on its bed of rice to the puffy lemon soufflé. Jason told Kim that they'd have their coffee in the library, then he held Linda's chair, put his arm around her waist and led her into the hall.

She sat on the sofa and Jason stood by the open French doors while Kim set up the tray. When Kim left, Jason went to the stereo. "Would you like some music? I have quite a library, but I must warn you, my entire collection is limited to JMR recordings."

"I had a feeling it would be." Linda smiled. She knew only too well how highly Jason valued those things which were his. "Anything soft would be fine. I'm not in the mood for rousing rock," she said.

After inserting a tape of classical music by a well-known pianist, he sat beside her on the sofa. Kim had placed a silver coffee pot and a tray of *petits fours* on the low table in front of Linda, and she poured a cup of coffee for Jason before doing the same for herself. A romantic melody filled the room, lacing the tension-laden atmosphere with sensual undertones. When Jason's sultry gaze met Linda's above the steam rising from his gold-rimmed cup she immediately blushed and dropped her eyes, breaking the contact. He sighed, put his cup on the table and walked back toward the open French doors, where he rested his arm against the door frame and studied the evening sky.

"Would you like to go for a ride?"

"Now . . . at night . . . where would we go? We've already had dinner."

"I know, but I feel like getting out, and I thought you might enjoy seeing some Hollywood landmarks. After all, you're still a relative newcomer to our fair city."

"Okay." Linda nodded. "I'd enjoy that. Just let me check on Andy; I haven't seen much of him today."

"Fine," Jason said. "I'll join you."

Mrs. Mason, who had taken Andy out to the garden

earlier, was just about to put him to bed when Jason and Linda entered the nursery. Jason took the sleepy baby from her arms, kissed him gently on the cheek and handed him to Linda. She kissed him and hugged him to her breast before settling him in the crib and covering him with a soft blue baby blanket. Then, after saying good night to Mrs. Mason, Jason put his arm over Linda's shoulder and led her from the room.

Linda edged closer to him, reacting to the intimacy she had felt when Jason had handed Andy to her and watched quietly while she put him to bed. No matter how much she wanted to hate Jason for what he had done she couldn't deny that Andy was a powerful bond fighting against that hatred. Jason seemed to feel the same way, because his arm tightened over her shoulder as they walked to the car.

The white Mercedes left Beverly Hills and traveled along Hollywood Boulevard until the surrounding area became more commercial; Linda thought it even looked slightly seedy. "This isn't at all what I had imagined Hollywood would look like."

Jason laughed. "That makes you like most tourists. They think Hollywood is the same as it was forty years ago, when all the buildings were new and super-stars lived in the surrounding hills. Unfortunately, the buildings got old and most movie companies moved their executive offices to Santa Monica, Beverly Hills or Universal City. JMR Industries is located in Century City. That's a whole new complex of apartment houses, office buildings and entertainment centers that weren't even here years ago when Hollywood was in its heyday. So Hollywood has grown old, and it's gotten run-down, but it's still the movie capital of the world to most people."

High in the hills, above the buildings and freeways, a huge sign spelled out Hollywood. Jason saw Linda staring at the illuminated display.

"The original developer of Hollywood erected that sign as a sales tool for his new homes tract, Hollywoodland, but the 'land' soon disappeared. The old wooden sign began falling apart in the early part of the 1970's. It became dangerous and had to be torn down, but it was such an integral part of the

Southern California scene that a committee was formed to raise funds to construct a new sign. That well-lit steel sign is the result of the committee's efforts, and the Hollywood sign remains a landmark."

Jason parked the car in a small lot on Hollywood Boulevard, then took Linda's hand and led her along the street. Terrazzo stars, outlined in bronze, were embedded in the pavement at regularly spaced intervals. Each star bore the name of a famous entertainment-industry personality. "This is the Walk of Fame," Jason explained. "Well-deserved recognition is shown to outstanding entertainers for their achievements in the industry by awarding them a bronze star in the pavement of Hollywood Boulevard."

As they kept walking, Linda bent her head to catch all the famous names listed beneath her feet. Her eyes were still glued to the ground when the shiny bronze stars gave way to concrete blocks with impressed footprints. She looked at Jason in surprise and he smiled back at her.

"The famous Grauman's Chinese Theater. It was built by Sid Grauman in 1927. When it first opened it was the most elegant theater in all of Hollywood, and lots of famous movies had their premieres here; some still do. It derives its name from the fact that it's decorated entirely in Chinese motifs."

Linda looked at the pagodalike structure, then back at the sidewalk. "But what are all these footprints?"

"These footprints represent the epitome of success in Hollywood. Space is limited, so only the most famous stars are asked to leave their imprint under the marquee of this theater."

Joining other tourists engaged in the same activity, Linda pored over the pavement at the front of the theater. She tried fitting her shoe into the print of several famous actresses and laughed when she read the autograph beside the one that fit. There were handprints beside the footprints of some famous child stars, and the most amusing items were the pawprints of well-known canine stars.

Jason led her to the photo-filled showcases that decorated the entrance to the theater. "The names of many Academy

Award winners are displayed in these showcases. You might say that this theater is a monument to all the people who made the film industry great."

They looked around some more, then went back to the car. As he drove through the streets, Jason pointed out rundown hotels and apartment buildings that had once been the homes of prominent members of the movie industry.

"No matter how shabby Hollywood may become, it will always represent film glamour and exotic movie stars to the rest of the world." Jason turned to Linda. "I hope you enjoyed my little tour. How about a nightcap before we go home?"

Linda smiled. "That would be nice."

Jason drove down Sunset Boulevard, parked the car near a small storefront restaurant and led her inside. They were shown to a table near the front of the stage and Jason ordered two Irish coffees. The atmosphere was very informal, and Linda found herself chuckling at the wry humor of the young comedian who was performing.

"Who is he?" she asked Jason. "I've never heard of him."

"Very few people have. A famous comedian got the idea of opening a workshop where beginners could get a start and seasoned entertainers could try out new acts. They're happy for a chance to rehearse, and the audience benefits by seeing a performance before it's ever shown on television or in an expensive nightclub."

The stage lights dimmed, and a new entertainer appeared. Linda immediately recognized him as a famous comedian who specialized in getting laughs by insulting his audience. His act always made her uncomfortable, and she became uneasy as he began slandering various racial and ethnic groups. When he saw that he wasn't getting a good reaction to that type of entertainment he began to ridicule members of the audience. Suddenly his eyes landed on Jason and he smiled broadly.

"And there he is, folks, Mr. Jason Reynolds, master of dreams, the Lothario of the entertainment world. Every day another beautiful young girl on his arm, and this one is really pretty. But I wonder, Jason, does Monique know about this little cutie? I understood she had you all staked out for herself."

Linda's face grew warm and tears welled in her eyes. She stood up abruptly, knocking her chair over in her haste to leave the nightclub. Jason reached quickly into his pocket and threw some money on the table, then he dashed after her, catching up with her as she neared the car. His hands grasped her upper arms and turned her toward him.

"Linda, let me explain."

"There's nothing to explain. . . . I behaved like a child in there. I'm sorry if I embarrassed you."

"You didn't embarrass me, Linda. That man doesn't know what he's saying. He'll do anything to get a reaction. He's especially insensitive when he's having a hard time winning the audience. Tomorrow morning he'll call up to apologize for what he did and tell me he was only joking, but you won't be around to hear it. Won't you believe me?"

Linda shook her head. "What I believe doesn't matter. I'm just not sophisticated enough to fit into your circle."

Jason brought her toward him and tried to hold her against his chest, but she placed her hands between them. "Please don't, Jason. I can't live like this. Just take me home. . . . I'm very tired."

He released her and waited while she settled herself in her seat, then he paid the parking attendant and started up the car. The trip home was accomplished in absolute silence. Linda spent most of the time staring at her hands, which were clasped tightly in her lap. When she ventured a covert glance at Jason she noted that his hawklike features were set in bitter determination and that his knuckles were white from clenching the steering wheel. His eyes stared straight ahead, following the road, never once turning in her direction.

When they reached home Linda didn't get out of the car immediately. For some reason Jason's cold disregard was more upsetting than it had ever been. She hoped he'd say something to break the tension, but he sat there silently, his hands still resting on the wheel. Finally when Linda realized that he was waiting for her to go, she left the car.

As she went into her room and prepared for bed she

considered her situation. She knew that Jason expected her to adjust to his way of life and content herself with a marriage where she would bear his children and he would continue seeing beautiful women like Monique. But she could never be happy in a marriage that wasn't based on love and absolute fidelity. She knew that she loved Jason, but she also knew that he didn't—couldn't—return that love, and a one-sided love just wasn't enough, so she had to leave him before he hurt her again.

The sound of tires crunching against the brick driveway brought Linda to the window in time to see the white Mercedes moving swiftly toward the gate. There was little doubt in Linda's mind as to where Jason was going. He didn't intend to waste time arguing with her when another, more attractive woman was so eager to satisfy his needs.

She lay in bed staring at the ceiling, unable to sleep. The clock ticked well into the early hours of the next morning, and Jason still hadn't returned. Finally slumber beckoned and she dozed off without ever hearing if the white Mercedes had returned home.

The brash ring of the alarm clock woke her while she was still deep in the grasp of a tormented dream. She reached out to shut it off and go back to sleep when she remembered that she had to be at Karizma Records by ten o'clock. After showering quickly, she dressed in an apricot linen wrap-around skirt with a matching scoop-necked blouse. A short, gold chain circled her neck and she tied her long, blond hair at the nape with an apricot silk ribbon. Glancing at her watch, she realized how late it was; she didn't even have time to stop at the nursery to see Andy. Once more she regretted the demands a career would make on the time she had for him, but under the circumstances she didn't have any choice. Not if she really wanted to show Jason that she was as capable a woman as his darling Monique.

The keys to the station wagon were still in her purse, so she ran down the steps and out the front door. The engine started easily and in no time at all she was driving toward Santa Monica, where Karizma Records had its corporate offices. It was a clear day, since the Santa Ana winds blowing across the valley had kept the smog from collecting at the base of the San Gabriel Mountains and covering the Los Angeles basin with its acrid brown vapors. Linda drove down the winding road and admired the majestic beauty of distant mountains whose lofty peaks had previously been hidden beneath a film of smog.

The attendant nodded in greeting as he lifted the gate to the parking lot and motioned Linda to a vacant spot. Once again she slipped her wedding band into her purse before going inside. This time she didn't go to Steve's office, but went directly to the recording studio where the Sapphires were waiting.

Jeff waved to her. "We're still working on the album we started last week, but we thought it might be good for you to listen to us and catch our style. Then you'll know how to blend in when we start singing together. We'll go ahead and use you for a few cuts on this album, okay?"

Linda sat in the recording studio and listened to the pulsating beat of the group's music. It was rock, but somehow its tonal quality differed from the hard rock currently dominating the industry. The lyrics were soft and poetic, and the music had the lilt of an old English folk song. She had learned that the Sapphires wrote their own songs and was pleased to find that their music was very similar to her own.

As she sat in the recording booth Linda learned that the sound heard on the record was more than just the Sapphires' singing. The technicians in the booth worked the sophisticated electronic machinery to get the exact mixture of tones they wanted. They listened through earphones and adjusted each control until the sound was exactly right, then they played it back for the group's approval; if something was still off they adjusted more dials and tried to get a better mix. It took the combined talents of the Sapphires and the technicians to produce the record that would, they hoped, find its way into the homes of millions of devoted fans.

Terry wasn't too happy with the first take. "I think we need more of an intro; the first verse could move a little faster, and the bridge could be stronger, too. We need more feel for the music; the lyrics should be softer."

They did another take and played that back. "It's good, nearly perfect," Bill said, "except the mix might be dragging on the bottom. It needs something. More bass, maybe. I'm not sure."

"Let me play with it," the head engineer said. "I'll see what I can do."

A half hour later the mix was exactly right, and when the red silence light dimmed, the Sapphires put down their instruments and began relaxing. Linda stood and stretched and Terry motioned for her to join them on the recording floor.

"That's in the pocket," Bill said. "What do you think? Will your singing fit with ours?"

Linda nodded. "I think so; I'm a rhythm and blues singer, but somehow I think my music is going to blend with yours. I write my own songs and I think your rock beat might be the perfect accompaniment to my mood music."

"That's great," Bill said. "You'll have to play some for us later. But right now I'm starving. Why don't we take a lunch break and talk about our *next* album?"

Chapter Seven

They had lunch at a small restaurant that specialized in various types of stew served in individual cast-iron kettles. While enjoying her lamb stew and crisp, crusty French bread, Linda mentioned that she had done some singing in Laguna Beach. Jeff and Bill nodded, saying they were familiar with the small coffeehouse where she had worked.

"That's a good place," Jeff said. "They don't pressure you, let you do your own thing. The Palominos started there, didn't they?"

Linda nodded. "That's what I've heard. They were gone by the time I came, but I understand they were just about to break up when one of their demo's was picked up by Artown."

"That's what happened to us," Terry said. "We used our last few bucks to rent fifteen minutes at Rick Casey's studio. We only had time for two takes, but we must have clicked, because Steve heard the record and offered us a contract."

"If we hadn't hit," Jeff said, "we would have broken up. Things were so bad that we weren't even making rent money."

"Don't I know," Linda said, remembering the times she had gone without eating.

"People only hear about the big money that recording stars make," Terry said. "They don't realize how many years of hard work and hard times go into reaching the top."

"Well, I think we're going to make it this time," Bill said. "Our album will have the right combo of rhythm and blues and rock and roll. We've got a sophisticated new image and"—he looked at Linda—"a beautiful lady partner."

"Thank you," Linda said. "I'm really happy to be part of the Sapphires."

"And we're happy to have you," Jeff said, as the waitress came around to refill their coffee cups.

They had finished their meal and were preparing to leave when the door to a private room at the back of the restaurant swung open and shrill feminine laughter pierced the air. Linda turned and saw Monique Le Paige reaching up to stroke her escort's cheek in appreciation for whatever remark he had just made. She immediately recognized him as the handsome leading man of a popular television series, but she didn't have time to think about what he was doing here with Monique. The one thing she was sure of was that she didn't want Monique seeing her with the Sapphires, because she was positive that the sultry star would lose no time telling Jason what she had seen. Linda couldn't let that happen; she had to think of something, anything, that would stop Monique from seeing her.

Sliding her hand across the table, she dropped her napkin to the floor and bent to retrieve it just as Monique's long, shapely legs went gliding past. Linda's face was hidden by the tablecloth, and by the time she lifted her head Monique was walking through the door. Breathing a sigh of relief, Linda sat back and put her napkin on the table.

She spent the afternoon in the rehearsal room with the Sapphires. They were anxious to hear her music, so she played two songs; when she was halfway through the third they made her stop.

"That's really good," Bill said. "Exactly what we're looking for. Let's hear it again."

She started to play and this time, when she went into the refrain, the others joined in and began playing variations of the major theme until the soft, haunting tones of Linda's music blended perfectly with the sharper beat of their own. Linda had always performed alone, accompanied only by her guitar, and she was amazed at how much richer her music sounded when played by an entire group.

"See how great we are together?" Jeff said, looking at Linda. "You make our rock music sound soft and sexy." He turned to Bill. "Try to keep that beat steady, but low. Let Linda's guitar take the lead, and make sure the instruments don't drown out our voices. I want those as the top sound—no lead singer, just four-part harmony—so we've really got to work at it, make everything blend. Okay, let's run through it again."

The afternoon passed quickly, and it was four o'clock before Linda even thought about the time. If she didn't leave now, Jason would be home before her. He was sure to ask where she had been, and that was something she wanted to avoid. She hated lying, even to Jason. She stood and reached for her guitar case. "I really have to leave."

Terry looked surprised. "It's early. We usually go out, have a few drinks, kick the song around until it sounds good to all of us."

Linda tugged nervously at her bottom lip. "I'm really sorry—I just can't stay. I have to be home by five. I'll be in early tomorrow." She picked up her bag.

Steve came down from the control room, where he had been for the last hour or so. "I guess I should have warned you boys," he said. "Linda likes to do things her own way. We'll just have to give her some time." He linked his arm with hers. "Come on, I'll walk you to the elevator."

"You make me sound awful," Linda said. "Wanting things my way." She shook her head. "That's not it at all." She hated the way she must look to Steve and the Sapphires—as if she were some sort of prima donna who put herself above the others, traipsing off to have a good time, leaving them to do all the work.

"Well, tell me how it is, then," Steve said, pressing the elevator button. "What's the story?"

Linda hated all this lying. It was bad enough that she had to lie to Jason; she didn't have to do it here. She reached into her purse, slipped on her ring, and held her finger out to Steve. "I'm married," she said.

"Isn't everybody?" Steve asked, quirking the corner of his mouth. "What's the big deal? Why all the intrigue?"

"I don't want my husband to know about this."

"Know about what?"

"The Sapphires—my singing with them—making a record."

"Why not? Is he some kind of creep?"

Linda smiled. "You might say that. He just wouldn't understand. . . . It's better this way."

Steve took her hands in his. "Does he understand anything about you?"

"Not really." Linda sighed, gently pulling her hands from his. "But that's my problem, not yours. I won't let it interfere with my work. If it does, I'll quit the group."

"Hey, nobody's pressing you. I'll explain to the boys; they'll understand. But this husband of yours must be some jerk. Doesn't he know how much money you could make?" He hesitated for a moment. "I don't know how bad things are, but if you're considering a divorce, you'd better get it now, before your record hits the street. This is a community-property state, and there's no point in giving Mr. Brown a cut."

Linda nodded. "I'll be in early tomorrow." She went into the elevator.

So Steve thought her husband's name was Brown. She hadn't told him that, hadn't lied to him, he had just made an assumption and she hadn't bothered to correct him. She smiled to herself as she walked to the car. Steve thought her husband was foolish not to be interested in the money she might make. If only he knew! Jason would be interested—very interested—but he wouldn't be happy. He was too smart not to know why she wanted the money.

She was nearly at her car when Steve caught up with her. "Wait a minute," he said, grabbing her arm. "What about a tour?"

"A tour? What tour?"

"The concert tour. Once we get this album going, we've got to push it. I've got a tour all lined up. How are you going to keep that from your husband?"

A tour. Linda's heart plunged to her stomach. She hadn't even thought about that. It would be hard enough to keep Jason from finding out about her daily trips to Santa Monica; she could never dream up an excuse for a tour. And Andy—

what would she do about Andy? She sighed helplessly. Every time her future looked bright someone came in to cut off the electricity. She didn't know what to do; she needed time to think about it. "I'll handle it," she told Steve. "Don't worry; I won't let you down." She smiled with a confidence she didn't feel.

She thought about the situation as she drove down Sunset Boulevard. Maybe there was an answer. If the album was as successful as everyone thought it would be, she could ask Steve for an advance just before the tour; then she could leave with Andy and Mrs. Mason, and by the time Jason found out about the tour, it would be too late for him to do anything because she and Andy would already be gone. And if she was earning enough money the courts would have to grant her custody; they usually ruled in favor of the mother, didn't they? Then Andy and Mrs. Mason could either come on tour with her or they could stay in the comfortable home she would buy for them. She smiled as she passed the freeway, confident that she had solved her problem.

Traffic was heavy and it was nearly five when Linda got home; she winced when she saw Jason's car already in the driveway, then quickly parked the station wagon behind the Mercedes and began walking to the house. When she reached the steps she saw Jason rounding the open portico with Andy in his arms. Andy giggled and reached out to Linda. She took him from Jason and kept moving toward the entry.

"You're out pretty late," Jason said. "Where were you?"

"The same as yesterday. I've been browsing through the stores." Why did he have to ask? She hated all this lying.

Jason held the door for her as they went into the house. "You left early. No one knew where you were and Mrs. Mason said you hadn't even stopped in to see Andrew. Plus you had Mrs. Smithers' car all day; that was hardly considerate of you. I'm glad you're getting out; I just wish you'd tell someone where you're going."

Linda shrugged. "I wanted to get an early start. The shops get crowded later on."

When she reached the nursery Mrs. Mason took Andy and

Linda continued to her room. Jason followed and settled himself in an easy chair by the window. "Did you have any better luck with your shopping today?"

"No, I'm still studying the new styles. I don't want to buy anything until I know what I want."

"Don't you think you should go with Barbara? She did offer. Maybe she could help you make up your mind. It seems like a colossal waste to spend all this time window shopping."

"You may be right, but I'd rather do it this way. I want to be sure I'm developing my own taste and not someone else's." She looked over at him, hoping he would leave; she was hot and tired and couldn't wait to get into the shower, but Jason seemed to be comfortably settled in the chair with no intention of moving.

She didn't know what to do; there was no way she could relax with Jason in the room. Being with him had made her nervous enough when she just had to worry about keeping a tight rein on her sensual responses; now that she had to contend with feelings of self-recrimination as well her discomfort was unbearable.

Yet what choice did she have? She couldn't accept the servile role Jason had planned for her because, if she did, she'd become just another one of his possessions. Now, more than ever, she was determined to do what she had set out to do when she first came to Los Angeles. She had to show Jason that she really had talents other than those which had caught his interest, and she couldn't let him know what she was doing because she was certain that if he found out he would try to stop her.

Yet, as much as she told herself that all this deceit was absolutely necessary, she couldn't help feeling guilty about the lies she was telling. A small inner voice insisted that maybe she was wrong, maybe Jason didn't deserve this treatment, maybe she should take a chance and tell him the truth. Then a louder voice reminded her of what had happened the last time she had taken a chance with Jason and warned her against repeating her folly.

Still, Jason did seem different from the man she thought he

was during the eighteen months they had been apart. She had always thought of him as arrogant, unfeeling and set in his ways. Yet there were so many times when his behavior contradicted these beliefs. She knew their relationship was based on threats and deception, and they argued constantly, yet no matter how angry Jason got with her, he always seemed ready to forgive and forget. This conciliatory attitude had never impressed her one way or another; she had always been too bitter to even consider Jason's friendly overtures, but tonight, probably to soothe her own guilty conscience, she felt she had to make an amicable move of her own. "Shall I change for dinner? Have you made plans which include me?"

"All my plans would include you," Jason said, "if only you'd let them. You're the one who keeps nursing a grudge and doesn't want a normal marriage." He shrugged. "But I must be a glutton for punishment, because I have made plans for tonight. There's a private dinner club that I think you'll enjoy." He rose from the chair. "I'll give you some time to get ready and meet you in the library." He went into the adjoining room.

Linda showered quickly and changed into a simple white jersey dress with a delicately pleated cowl neck. A slim metallic belt girded her waist and the slightly flared skirt flowed softly over her hips and legs. High-heeled, bronze-toned sandals completed her outfit. The skirt swirled, clinging to her legs as she walked into the library.

Jason was sitting behind the desk, reading some papers he had taken from his still-open attaché case, and the rigid lines of his face relaxed in approval when she walked toward him. He put down his pen and leaned back in his chair, studying her appearance. "You look lovely. I can't see anything wrong with your taste in clothing."

Linda smiled. "Thanks, Jason, but Miss Jenson bought this outfit, too. It's probably more sophisticated than what I would have chosen. That's why I still feel uneasy about buying anything just yet."

Jason stood, threw the papers back into his attaché case

and closed it. He was wearing a navy mohair suit and the dull sheen of his light blue shirt highlighted his aquiline features. Linda stared at him and couldn't help remembering how spellbound she had been the first time she had seen him at that crowded studio party. She had thought then that he was the handsomest man she had ever seen, and seeing him now only reinforced that first impression. A quiver of possessive pride moved through her body at the thought that they were married, but she squelched it by asking herself what good the marriage was if Jason didn't love her. Jason broke into her depressing ruminations by coming from behind the desk and putting his arm around her waist.

"Let's go. We don't want to be late." He bent toward her as he spoke and his breath warmed the inner curve of her ear.

Kim was waiting at the front door. "I thought I'd let Kim drive tonight," Jason said. "That way I can relax."

They rode through the Hollywood Hills until they came to a secluded estate surrounded by huge trees and overgrown shrubbery. Jason handed Kim a card, which he showed to the gateman, then they drove up a steep hill and stopped in front of a large Victorian house trimmed with turrets and gingerbread. A red-jacketed valet rushed up to open the car doors.

Jason's arm circled Linda's waist as he guided her toward the wide wooden veranda. A man wearing a black silk top hat and cape greeted them at the entry. The interior was shadowy, illuminated only by the glass-encased candles flickering on each table. Jason and Linda were led to a table fronting on a stagelike platform and, after checking Linda's preferences, Jason ordered drinks and two steak dinners. The food was good, their conversation surprisingly friendly and free from tension, and Jason was smiling as Linda finished her last spoonful of baked Alaska.

"What do you think of this place?" he asked.

"It's very different. Is it the same kind of place as the one we were in last night?" she asked, remembering the comedian's painful taunts.

"Similar; they do feature some new acts here." He reached across the table and covered her hand with his. "But there's not the slightest chance that you'll be embarrassed here. Please forget about last night; I'll never let it happen again. The man's a complete clod. I was so upset that I couldn't sleep; I went to the office and worked through the night."

Linda lowered her head and sipped her coffee. He hadn't gone to Monique. She felt as if a weight had been lifted from her chest. She wanted to do exactly as Jason said, forget about last night, never remember it, pretend it never happened. "The meal was delicious. I didn't realize there were so many good restaurants in Los Angeles."

"Why should that surprise you? We have one of the world's most pleasant climates with moderate temperatures, low humidity and almost constant sunshine. A lot of very wealthy people live here, so it's only logical that we'd have some very fine restaurants."

A spotlight danced across the stage and another man dressed in a top hat and cape walked out. A young woman wearing an attractive sequined outfit joined him, and they began doing magic tricks. Two more acts followed and they, too, performed magic of one sort or another. Then the spotlight dimmed and Jason turned to Linda. She was still clapping.

"I'm glad you liked it."

Linda nodded. "They were so good, Jason. What type of place is this? I've never heard of it."

"It's a private club. You need a card to get in, and most of the prominent people in the film industry belong. Professional magicians perform each evening, so in addition to the fine food the guests enjoy a unique type of entertainment. Later on the magicians come around and perform right at the tables; it's a good idea, isn't it?"

Just as Linda was about to answer, icy fingers tapped her bare arm. "Jason, how nice to see you and your lovely little wife." Linda shuddered as Monique Le Paige smiled down at her. "Did you tell Jason that we ran into each other this afternoon?"

Oh, no, Linda thought, not now; please don't ruin everything now, not when the evening has been going so pleasantly. She shook her head. "No, I forgot to mention it, but he does know I was out shopping." Linda held her breath. She was sure Monique understood what she was asking. Now she was at Monique's mercy. Either the woman would remain silent or she would shatter Linda's future by telling Jason what she had seen.

Chapter Eight

Monique arched one perfectly shaped eyebrow. "You made some interesting purchases on your shopping expedition."

Jason looked surprised. "On the contrary, Monique, Linda didn't buy anything. She only went window shopping."

"Well, then, I should correct myself by saying that she was looking in some very interesting windows." Monique's glance shifted back to Linda. "Jason, you must excuse your lovely wife for a few minutes. I think we'd both like to freshen up and have a little chat. We won't be long." She started walking toward the ladies' lounge, indicating that Linda should follow.

Once they were inside the rococo red and gold powder room Monique handed several folded bills to the attendant and explained that they wanted to be alone. When the woman had gone Monique motioned Linda toward the small settee and seated herself on a red velvet chaise.

"Well, my dear, we seem to be involved in a very interesting situation. Jason and I were getting on quite well until you came along; now, for some stupid reason, he's brought you, the well-hidden wife, back from who-knows-where. He's determined to play the devoted husband and I've been having a hard time making him notice that I'm anything more than just a good draw at the box office. But you've been playing around behind his back, and I don't think he'd be pleased to find that his wife has been amusing herself with other men. Is that why he threw you out in the first place? Did you use the baby to make him take you back? Did you promise to change?"

Linda's startled face reflected her disbelief. "What are you talking about? I haven't been seeing other men behind Jason's back."

"Really?" Monique laughed. "How would you explain that interesting little scene at the Stew Pot? And if it was so innocent, why did you lie and tell Jason you'd been shopping?"

Linda grimaced. "I can't explain. All I can say is that it's not what you think." She stood and began pacing the room.

"Sit down; you're making me nervous. What I think doesn't really matter. The important thing is what Jason will think when he finds out."

Linda's eyes narrowed. "And you'll be only too happy to tell him, won't you?"

Monique placed a cigarette in her long holder and shrugged. "I have no reason not to, do I?"

Linda pursed her lips. "Okay. What do you want? Money?"

A delicate puff of smoke drifted from Monique's lips and she smiled. "Does it look as if I need your money?" She held out her jeweled fingers and wrists. "Obviously not, but we can still make a deal if you're willing to be sensible. Apparently you don't care for Jason, although for the life of me I can't understand why you'd prefer anyone else. Still, there's no accounting for taste. Anyway, I'm very interested in him, so I think we can strike a bargain. I'll keep your little secret if you don't interfere when I make my play for Jason. In fact, you can help by turning him off. He'll have to go somewhere, and I'll be waiting in the wings, ready, willing and more than able."

"Are you suggesting that I throw my husband into your arms? You expect me to destroy my own marriage?"

"Why not?" Monique shrugged. "You don't love Jason. Your romantic interests obviously lie with younger, scruffier types. Why mess up my chances? You wouldn't be losing anything you wanted yourself. Besides, what makes you think that Jason would still want anything to do with you once I've told him what I've seen? He's a proud man, and I don't think he'd be thrilled with a wife who's little better than a groupie. And what a group. Are those nonentities the best you can do? Or did you feel that obscurity was some form of protection? That Jason wouldn't learn about your cheating?''

"Stop it, Monique; I haven't been cheating, but I don't want Jason to know what I've been doing—not yet. If you tell him now, you'll ruin everything." Linda turned and looked in the mirror. Monique's reflection smiled evilly back at her, telling Linda that she wouldn't hesitate to march outside and tell Jason what she had seen—in fact, she'd probably add her own little spicy embellishments. Linda remembered what Jason had said about throwing her out and keeping Andy if he ever thought she was seeing another man. She couldn't risk letting Monique carry out her threat. She slammed her fist down on the marble vanity. "All right, I don't have any choice. I'll go along with your little scheme, but only until I get things settled and can tell Jason the truth myself."

"Whatever you say." Monique stood and ran her hands over her satin-clad hips. "We'd better get back now. We don't want Jason wondering about us."

Jason was talking to one of the magicians when they returned to the table. He stood to hold Linda's seat out for her. Monique lingered and rested her hand on Jason's shoulder.

"Jason, darling," she said, "I've just invited you and Linda to my house for a nightcap, but she says she's too tired. She doesn't mind if you come alone. You will, won't you? We have so many things to discuss, and your office is so stuffy. I just can't get comfortable there."

Jason glanced at Linda. "If Linda is tired, we'll take a raincheck. I've had a busy day myself."

Linda tugged nervously at her bottom lip. "I really don't mind if you go, Jason. I'll feel like a wet blanket if I ruin your evening. Besides, Monique is probably right. It would be a good chance for the two of you to discuss business. I'd only be bored; you're much better off going alone."

Jason's eyes narrowed and he stared at Linda coldly. "All right . . . if that's what you really want." He stood and helped her out of the chair she had only just taken. "I'll tell

Kim to take you home. He can pick me up at Monique's later."

Monique flashed a triumphant smile. "Much later, Jason, much, much later." She linked her arm through his and waved to Linda.

Kim drove Linda home and, after she went inside, she heard the car head back down the driveway. He was on his way to Monique's, to wait for Jason. Linda wondered how long a wait he'd have. She shook her head; she didn't want to think about it. The whole subject was just too depressing. After closing her door she began to undress. She washed, changed into her nightgown and she slid between the cool silk sheets, but she was too nervous to sleep; her thoughts were too confused. She wanted to hate Jason for what he had done to her. He had taken advantage of her innocence, ruined her life, threatened to take Andy from her. She had a right to be angry; she would never forgive him, not ever, she told herself. She was, she silently insisted, happy that Monique wanted him because she wanted nothing to do with him; she didn't care who he slept with so long as it wasn't her. She did not—she absolutely *did not*—love him.

Why, then, did she feel so bad about the way the evening had ended? Probably because it had started off so pleasantly, and up until Monique had come to their table she had really enjoyed being with Jason. Still, how could she like being with Jason if she hated him so much? Unless, maybe she didn't hate him quite so much anymore? Of course she didn't love him, she had certainly been wrong about that, but that didn't mean she had to hate him, either. Maybe he really was sorry about what had happened. But then, why had he been so demanding? Why had he threatened to take Andy from her if she didn't marry him?

Things were happening too fast. She was uncertain of her own feelings and nothing made any sense. But the one thing she was sure of was that no matter how she felt about Jason, she didn't want Monique in the picture.

She remembered his touch, how gentle he could be when he held her in his arms. She remembered how his hands and lips had caressed her body that first night, the night when

Andy had been conceived. Andy . . . Jason had taken her
virginity, but he had given her Andy. She didn't even have to
think about which she would rather have. And despite her
telling Jason that she wished she could erase that night,
wished she had never let him make love to her, she knew it
wasn't true. Andy had been born from their lovemaking, and
he was the joy of her life.

It seemed as if she had spent a sleepless eternity staring at
the ceiling, but her bedside clock told her it had been just
over an hour when the sound of tires rolling over the brick
driveway brought her reveries to an end. It was too soon; she
wondered if Jason had decided to spend the night with
Monique and sent Kim home alone. Then the opening and
closing of car doors, followed by Jason's and Kim's conversation, told her that Jason *had* returned. He had certainly spent
very little time with Monique.

Maybe Jason had been telling the truth. After all, Monique
admitted that he wasn't being as attentive as she would have
liked. If that was the case, then Linda had been as unfair to
Jason as he had been to her. In her vindictive rage she had
refused to listen to his explanations, just as he hadn't listened
to hers. Well, what would happen if she tried now? She shook
her head silently. What good would it do? Even if her feelings
toward Jason had changed, she was trapped by the deceptive
web she had spun, and now Monique was tugging at the
threads, tightening them until they had become a noose
around Linda's neck.

She had to keep her promise to Monique because one word
from the actress would convince Jason that Linda was guilty
of the very thing she had accused him of. He would never
forgive her; he might even be angry enough to divorce her
and take custody of Andy. She just couldn't take the chance;
she'd have to play along with Monique until she had a
successful career. Then she could tell him the truth and hope
that he accepted it.

The entry door closed and steps sounded on the stairway.
Linda waited for Jason to pass her room and listened as he
went toward the nursery. She heard that door open and close

a few minutes later, then Jason went to his own room. The sounds of his movements filtered through the wall and Linda heard him prepare for bed. Suddenly his steps drew closer and the knob on the adjoining door clicked.

Softly glimmering light flowed through the open door, lighting Jason's path as he walked to her bed. Linda watched him through lowered lashes. He wore only brown silk pajama bottoms and as he came closer she could see the dark hair curling over his broad chest. The potent masculinity of his movements sent tremors through Linda's body and she closed her eyes against the tingles of desire that were prickling deep within her.

He stopped and looked down at her silently. Then she felt the mattress sag beneath his weight as he seated himself at the edge of the bed and began stroking her long blond hair away from her face. An uncontrollable shiver surged through her body and she couldn't conceal it from him. He was too close; his hand was on her face and her quivering flesh met his like a lover seeking satisfaction.

"I didn't think you were sleeping. Your breathing was too even. Open your eyes, Linda; I'm not going to hurt you." Dipping his head, he kissed her eyelids until they opened.

Looking down at her, he tenderly traced her features, circling her eyes, lightly stroking across the bridge of her nose. "Poor Linda, do you hate me so that you'd send me to Monique? Have I frightened you that much? Are you so afraid to let me make love to you again?"

Linda warmed to his sensitive caresses. He wanted her; he had always wanted her, for whatever reason. And she had wanted him from the very first moment she saw him, had kept wanting him until his vicious accusations had turned desire to hate and made her want never to see him again. But had she really hated him, or had her love been hovering just beneath the surface all those months, waiting for his touch to reawaken it and make her want him again? And she did want him. She couldn't deny that. But what about her promise to Monique? What would Jason do if he believed Monique's story? And even if Linda explained—told him the truth—

would that be any better? How would he like learning that she had joined the Sapphires so she could make enough money to take Andy away from him? He wouldn't like it at all; in fact, he'd hate her as much as she had hated him.

If she let him make love to her tonight and Monique carried out her threat she could lose everything—Jason, Andy, her career—everything. She couldn't risk it. She had to do as Monique wanted. "Jason, please, I'm really tired. You didn't have to rush home. I understand about Monique; she's very attractive. Any man would find her hard to resist."

Jason lifted her, holding her to his chest with one arm while the other resumed its gently evocative stroking. "Monique is very attractive, but not for me. I'll never know why, but it's you I want and need." His lips nuzzled her earlobe and traveled down her arched neck while his hand slipped the nightgown straps off her shoulders, exposing her lush, pink-tipped breasts to his questing lips.

Her body was filled with an uncontrollable desire to let him proceed toward the end they both desired, but she knew she couldn't, not with Monique's threat hanging in the air. Pressing her hands against his chest she fought down the urge to bury her fingers in the short, curling hairs. She pulled away and brought the straps back over her shoulders. "No, Jason, please, we can't do this."

He didn't try to force her; he just leaned back and studied her silently. "Why not?" he asked in a ragged voice. "We're married."

Linda shrank back toward the headboard, away from Jason. "Only because of Andy. We don't love each other."

His broad hand reached out to grasp her upper arm. "It's because of him that I'm trying so hard, because of him and because of us. We are him, and he is us. We're all a part of each other now. We need each other. Can't you see that? Why must you fight me like this? I can feel your body responding, telling me what we could have, what we *should* have. Why won't you listen?"

"I am listening, and you haven't said anything." Not anything she wanted to hear. If he told her he loved her she would forget about Monique's threats and throw herself into the delight of his arms. But the word hadn't crossed his lips or, undoubtedly, his mind.

"I haven't said anything? What do you want me to do, get down on my knees and beg?" He made a fist and pounded it into the palm of his other hand. "Well, I'm not going to, so you can just forget that."

"I've never asked you to beg. I've never asked you for anything."

"That's right," he agreed cynically. "You never have, have you? You just took. You took my son and kept him hidden. I would never have seen him, never have known he existed, if you'd had your way."

Linda looked down at the blanket. There was nothing she could say. Jason was right; she couldn't deny it.

"Well, from now on we're doing things my way. I won't argue any more tonight, but this isn't the end. I'm not giving up. I've already told you my plans for Andrew; he'll have a normal family life, complete with brothers and sisters, and you'll do your part to provide them." He stormed out of the room.

Linda waited a few minutes, then turned on the bedside lamp. It was pointless to try to sleep. She was much too upset. Jason meant what he said. He didn't love her; he had only married her because of Andy. He loved his son and wanted him to have everything, including brothers and sisters. When he had run out of patience he'd take her and use her just as he had before. He might make her enjoy it in the end, but it would be just the same. At first she had been the object of his lust; now she was the mother he wanted for his children. Mutual love never entered into their relationship; if it had, Monique's threat wouldn't matter at all.

Monique. Linda's eyes widened in realization. That was probably why Jason had broken up with Monique. She was definitely not the motherly type. That's why he wants me, Linda thought, so he can have more children. Well, I won't do it! Much as I love Andy, I'm not going to let Jason turn me into his baby factory. This time I won't let Jason have his way. But to fight Jason I need money, money Steve promised I could get by singing with the Sapphires. Leaning back on the pillow, she crossed her fingers and prayed that he was right.

The studio was buzzing with conversation when Linda walked in the next morning. "What's going on?" she asked Terry.

He stroked his beard and shrugged. "A business problem, nothing that concerns us. Let the moguls like Steve worry about that; we're artists." He began tuning his bass.

"I guess you're right," Linda said, and she spent most of the morning rewriting her lyrics until the rest of the group was satisfied. They were so involved in their work that they didn't want to go out for lunch and had sandwiches sent in. Linda was happy they were eating in; there was less chance to run into anybody that way, anybody meaning Monique. The day passed quickly and, before she knew it, it was four o'clock. She stood and stretched.

"It's getting late; I've got to go," she said. "I'm out of creative ideas anyway." She picked up her handbag and walked to the elevator. The door opened and Steve stepped out. His face was tired and drawn, and his suit looked as if he had slept in it.

"What's wrong, Steve? You look exhausted."

"Business problems, nothing to worry your pretty little head about. Unless you'd like to help me relax over cocktails?" He waited expectantly.

"Sorry, Steve, I just can't. I told you I have to be home early."

"The mysterious Mr. Brown. He really has you under his thumb, doesn't he? Have you thought about what I said? A divorce, I mean."

"I'm not ready, Steve, not yet."

"Well, don't wait too long. And if you ever have any problems, remember I'm here."

Linda walked into the elevator. "Thanks, Steve, I appreciate that more than you know."

* * *

A small yellow Porsche was in the driveway when she parked the station wagon, which she continued to use, and for a minute Linda thought that Jason had company. But the white Mercedes wasn't there, so it couldn't be anyone visiting Jason. Looking more closely at the car, she noticed that it was brand new and didn't even have permanent license plates yet; she wondered who it belonged to.

She heard laughter coming from the back of the house and walked around to find Miss Jenson chatting with Mrs. Mason while Andy gurgled and reached up, trying to catch a passing flock of low-flying birds. Miss Jenson stood as Linda approached.

"Ah, there you are. I understand you've been getting acquainted with Rodeo Drive. Did you buy anything? Mr. Reynolds said you've mostly been browsing."

Linda shook her head and bent to pick up Andy. "That's about it. I've just been looking around. Besides, the things you bought are so beautiful that I won't need anything new for quite a while."

Miss Jenson smiled. "It's not hard to have good taste when you're shopping with your husband's kind of money. I only selected the clothing, you can thank him for buying it. And if you're pleased with the clothing, just wait until you see what I've brought you today." She rose and signaled for Linda to follow her to the front of the house. Then she dangled some car keys and pointed to the Porsche. "There she is. Isn't she a beauty? And she's all yours. Mr. Reynolds asked me to pick it up for you."

Linda was speechless. She handed Andy to Mrs. Mason and slipped behind the wheel. "I don't know what to say. I've never driven a sports car before." She ran her hand over the soft black leather seats. "This is beautiful. Thank you, Miss Jenson."

Miss Jenson laughed. "Don't thank *me;* I'm only the delivery girl. Mr. Reynolds ordered it for you; he's the one you have to thank. Well, I'd better be going." She started to walk away, then turned back to Linda. "Before I forget, Mr. Reynolds called to say he's working on something very important; he won't be home until late. He asked me to tell you to have dinner without him; he'll eat at the office."

Linda got out of the car and took Andy back from Mrs. Mason. The older woman looked at them fondly. "You're very lucky, Linda. Your husband loves you and Andy very much. I can see that when he looks at you. I'm so glad you got together again. I don't know what would have happened if you hadn't. You were getting so thin and tired."

They walked into the kitchen where Mrs. Smithers was preparing dinner and Linda suggested that since Jason wouldn't be home they could all eat together. It had been a long time since she had eaten with Andy and she wasn't looking forward to a solitary meal in the massive dining room.

While Linda fed Andy Mrs. Mason washed up and Mrs. Smithers prepared their meal. As soon as Andy had finished and was munching contentedly on a teething biscuit Mrs. Smithers began serving their dinner. Linda found the cold lobster salad a welcome change from the rich food Jason seemed to enjoy. They chatted amiably, and Linda felt more relaxed than she had been in weeks. When Andy began whining and throwing his biscuit on the floor she offered to take him upstairs and bathe him so Mrs. Mason could enjoy a second cup of coffee. Since she hadn't been alone with Andy for a long time she welcomed this opportunity.

Andy splashed and kicked in the tub, then closed his eyes without a whimper when she finally put him in his crib. She was stuffing his soiled clothing into the hamper when Mrs. Mason came in and said she would take over. Linda thanked her and went to her own room.

By nine o'clock she had showered and changed for bed. Her body felt delightfully cool and clean beneath the low-cut spaghetti-strapped, sheer silk gown. She sat on the chaise longue and flipped through the pages of a fashion magazine that Miss Jenson had given her, but she was too restless to concentrate. Thinking that a cool drink would relax her, she decided to get some iced tea. Her nightgown had a matching robe made of a heavier fabric and, after fastening the tiny covered buttons which ran the length of the garment, she went down to the kitchen.

Mrs. Smithers had gone to her room, but had left a small night light on over the sink. Linda opened the refrigerator door, took out a pitcher of iced tea and sat down with some of Mrs. Smithers home-baked chocolate chip cookies. Someone had left a copy of *Variety*, the unofficial show-business newspaper, on the kitchen counter, and she began reading it with interest, looking for familiar names.

She was engrossed in the paper when a car drove up and stopped in front of the house. She heard Jason and Kim speak for a few moments, then the front door opened and she heard Jason's footsteps going slowly up the stairs. She decided to stay in the kitchen, thinking she'd give him a chance to get to bed before she went, and had just added some fresh tea to her glass when she heard footsteps racing down the stairway. Then the front door opened and closed.

Had Jason come home just to freshen up? Where was he going at this time of night? To Monique? If so, no matter what had kept him away earlier, *this* certainly wasn't a business conference. A jealous thorn began pressing against her heart, inflicting the same stinging misery she felt whenever she pictured Jason with Monique. But there wasn't anything she could do about it because, even if she were willing to become the wife Jason wanted, he would never be faithful to her. He only wanted her because he thought she'd be a suitable mother for his children, but Monique was the type of woman he was really attracted to—the kind he could fall in love with. She had known that from the very first time she met him. The one thing her experience with Jason had taught her was that, to a man, there was a world of difference between making love to a woman and being in love with her, and no matter how intimately Jason had caressed her body he had never said he loved her. Sighing, she picked up her iced tea and walked to the sink.

Again the front door opened and slammed shut. Now she became frightened. "Jason," she called and walked into the hall.

Jason was leaning against the door. His jacket and tie were off, his shirt collar was open, and his sleeves were rolled up to just below his elbow. His usually neat hair was tousled and his eyes were red and tired-looking. "I'm sorry, Linda; I didn't mean to slam the door, but the wind caught it, and it slipped out of my hand. Where were you?"

"In the kitchen." She held up the iced tea glass.

He took a deep breath, then exhaled. It sounded like a sigh of relief. "Do you think I could have some?" He motioned toward her glass. "My throat is parched." He followed her into the kitchen.

"Sit down, Jason," she said, holding a chair out for him. "Do you feel all right? I've never seen you like this; you look exhausted. Miss Jenson said you were working late, so we had dinner without you. She said you'd have something brought up to the office."

"We did, but the sandwiches tasted like cardboard and I was too involved in what I was doing to pay much attention to food."

"I think there's still some lobster salad in the refrigerator. Would you like some?"

"Sounds great, if you don't mind keeping me company."

Linda prepared some salad, warm rolls and butter and set them before Jason, then sat opposite him while he ate. "What happened? I heard you go upstairs, but then you went out again. Is anything wrong?"

Jason put his fork down and looked at her. "Kim drove me home, and a good thing, too; I was so tired, I would have fallen asleep behind the wheel. He parked the car and I sent him off to bed, then I went upstairs to check on you and Andrew. He's sound asleep, but I couldn't find you."

"What made you check on us?"

Jason's tired eyes melted into hers. "I always check on you before I go to sleep. Didn't you know that? I can't sleep until I'm sure my family is secure for the night. When you weren't in your room . . ." He shook his head but kept looking at her.

Linda lowered her eyes. She hadn't known that Jason checked on both Andy and her each night. Why would he do that . . . unless he cared? She thought about how tired he looked; the man opposite her was a different Jason from the one she hated and feared. Exhaustion had vanquished his arrogance and he seemed strangely tender and vulnerable. If her feelings about him had been ambivalent before, they were running in complete circles now. She looked up and saw that he had stopped eating and, using his arms as a pillow, was resting his head on the table. Quietly, she cleared the dishes, rinsed them and stacked them in the dishwasher. Then she returned to Jason, who was now fast asleep.

She couldn't let him spend the night sleeping in a hard kitchen chair; he'd be a mass of aches and pains when he woke. But she couldn't get him upstairs alone, and she didn't want to wake Kim. She flexed her fingers into his tensed shoulders, gently trying to wake him so she could help him upstairs. Sighing pleasurably, he lifted his head and looked at her.

"That feels good. . . . I didn't mean to fall asleep. . . . I'm not very good company tonight, am I?"

Linda kept stroking the tension-bound muscles of his broad back and he arched his neck like a sleek panther. "You're very tired, Jason. You should be in bed. If you spend the night here you won't be able to move in the morning. Do you think you're awake enough to let me help you to your room?"

Jason lifted himself from the chair, stretching his long arms as he did so. He flashed a weary smile at Linda. "I'm all right. You won't have to carry me up the stairs, but I would appreciate having someone to lean on."

Someone to lean on. The words echoed in Linda's ears. She had always thought of Jason as being too strong to need anyone, yet here he was asking for someone to lean on, asking for her help. Jason needed her. She trembled at the thought. Never had she felt so close to him.

He turned off the light and eased his arm along her waist, drawing her close to his side. She leaned against his shoulder and he bent his head, resting it on hers as they walked slowly upstairs. Opening the door to his room, she moved with him toward the bed and tried to free herself as he lowered himself to the mattress, but he held her firmly, pulling her down with him.

"Umm, thank you." His lips nuzzled the side of her neck

while the fingers of his free hand fumbled with the buttons on his shirt. "Damn," he said, letting the shirt go. "I can't handle this. I'm just too tired. I'll sleep in my clothes."

"You won't be comfortable," Linda said. "Here, let me help you." She shifted her body over his and began opening the buttons. "Lift yourself a little." She bent lower and tried to slip his left arm out of the sleeve. His right arm still circled her back, and it tightened, drawing her body down against him. "Jason, let me go."

"Shh . . . I only want to hold you; I'm too tired to do anything else." His naked left arm circled her body and stroked lightly over her back.

"Jason, you've got to get some rest." She tried to ignore the warm prickles his fingers were raising on her spine and reached down to pull his right arm out of his shirt sleeve. His chest hair curled into the valley between her breasts and she shuddered as a glow spread through her body.

"Shh," Jason said, stroking her back gently. "Don't be afraid. I'm not going to hurt you. I'm so tired; I need you next to me. You feel so good; just let me hold you. Please, stay until I fall asleep."

His eyes were closing even as he spoke and Linda couldn't refuse his plea. She let herself relax and placed her fingers at his temples, massaging them lightly until he fell asleep. Then she wriggled out of his arms and sat beside him, staring down at him as he lay quietly on his back. Suddenly she didn't want to leave him. She wanted to lie down next to him and wrap herself in the security of his arms. But how could she, after all she had said? Sighing, she swung her feet to the floor.

When she went to the foot of the bed and slipped his shoes off his lashes fluttered briefly, then closed again; his even breathing told her he had fallen into a deep sleep. Lifting the blanket at the foot of the bed, she covered him, hoping that he would sleep through the night and wake rested in the morning. She opened the adjoining door, but before walking through she turned to look back at Jason.

Sleep had softened his features and now, more than ever, he looked like Andy. She walked back to the bed and lifted her hand, holding it just above his face. Her fingers flexed with an intense desire to reach down and touch him, but she curled them into a fist and pressed them against her mouth.

He looked so young, so vulnerable. She wanted to slip beneath the covers, press her body close to his, hold him in her arms and comfort him. She knew how he felt, what it was like to be overworked and tired, but somehow she had never thought of Jason in that way. He had always seemed so strong, so powerful, practically indestructible. But lying on the bed, his hand pillowing his cheek, he looked more like an exhausted young boy than a domineering business tycoon. She sighed and lowered her hand. It didn't matter what she thought. It wasn't the first time her imagination had envisioned Jason as more human than he really was. That was why she had gone into his arms and welcomed his touch at their very first meeting.

She had been wrong then, and she was probably wrong now. But what if she weren't? She had changed, hadn't she? She had forgiven him; she no longer hated him. What if Jason had changed? Hadn't he said that he always checked on her before going to bed? Hadn't he gone looking for her? But why? Was he doing it because he loved her or because he was afraid of losing one of his possessions? She couldn't be sure, and until she understood how he really felt about her she couldn't think of telling him that her feelings for him had changed.

Her feet felt like rocks as she slowly made her way back to her own room. Her hand circled the doorknob and she started to close it, then she stopped and left it open. It seemed like the simplest way to show Jason that she didn't hate him quite as much as she used to. She didn't hate him at all.

She might just as well have closed the door for all the good it did her, because when she woke the next morning and peeked into his room Jason was gone. Sighing at the futility of her attempt to improve their relationship, she turned on the shower and started getting ready for her rehearsal with the Sapphires, but suddenly she wasn't so sure that she was doing the right thing. Even if he had disregarded the open door between their rooms, she couldn't forget how gently he had spoken to her last night.

She knew he loved Andy; perhaps, if she gave him enough time, he might learn to love her, too. And even if he didn't, at least she would have more of him than the memory of just one night. She remembered that he had said he wanted more children, children like Andy. The creation of a child was a powerful bond between a man and a woman. She knew that now. Could anything be more intimate? She doubted it. And Jason wanted more children—her children. Nerves knotted deep within her abdomen at the thought and she sank to the side of the bed, wondering if she should call Steve and tell him she couldn't continue with the Sapphires.

Then she remembered Monique's threat. Jason had been angry enough about her keeping Andy's birth from him. How would he feel when he found that she had been trying to take him away again? She shook her head and began to dress. Monique was right; there would be no reasoning with him. His pride would stop him from listening to any explanation she could offer. And he might very well force her to leave—alone—without Andy.

Just the thought of never seeing Andy again was more than she could bear, so she couldn't stop now. Things had gone too far; she just couldn't turn back. Maybe if the Sapphires were successful and she earned some money and a position of her own, maybe then Jason would see her as a mature woman he could love and respect. At least it was a chance, probably her only chance. She left the house and drove away in her sleek new Porsche.

The rehearsal went well, and Terry told Linda that he thought she was ready to cut her first song. He suggested that they could all benefit from a few days' rest before the actual recording began, and Linda welcomed the break because it meant she could spend some time with Andy. That was the one thing she really hated about working with the Sapphires; it kept her away from Andy.

After gathering their things the group left the building

together. Bill was a car buff and began asking Linda about the horsepower and mileage of the Porsche. She explained that she had just gotten the car and knew very little about it. They were still talking when a red Jaguar drove up and parked beside them. Steve Douglas got out, looking just as exhausted as he had the day before.

"You kids cutting out early?"

"Yeah," Jeff said. "We're about ready to record and we decided to take a few days' break before beginning."

Steve combed his fingers through his hair. "We'll have to start thinking about the record jacket. You guys have those sequined outfits from Tony Lamson, but we'll need something smashing for Linda." He thought for a minute. "Do you know Tony's shop on Rodeo Drive?"

"I can find it," Linda said.

"Good. I'll have my secretary arrange an appointment. Stop by and let him get started so you'll have something ready in time for the cover photos."

The Sapphires waved good-bye and headed for the van they shared; Linda slid behind the wheel of the Porsche. Steve's arm rested on the open door and his eyes raked the car's interior.

"Nice, very nice. Is it new?"

Linda nodded.

Steve smiled. "I take it the home situation is improving."

When Linda didn't answer, Steve continued. "Or maybe you have a generous friend?"

"It's just a car, Steve, and my personal problems are something I'll have to work out by myself." She smiled to take the edge off her words, then shut the door as he straightened away from the car. "I'll see Tony Lamson whenever you say." Waving, she drove off.

Jason didn't return until late that night, and if he stopped in then to check on Linda she was asleep and didn't notice. As usual he was gone before she woke, but for some reason she found herself missing what little daily contact they had had; oddly enough, even arguing with Jason seemed better than not seeing him at all. To take her mind off things she called Steve's secretary and discovered that she had an appointment with Tony Lamson at ten o'clock that morning, so she swung her feet off the bed and began getting ready. She dressed quickly, stopped in to see Andy and went down to breakfast.

Mrs. Smithers looked at her in surprise. "I'm glad to see that you're eating today. It's not healthy to skip breakfast as often as you do."

Linda smiled and sipped her orange juice. "Did Mr. Reynolds say that he'd be home for dinner?"

"No, he didn't, but Miss Jenson said she'd let me know as soon as possible."

Linda finished her coffee and put the cup in the dishwasher. "I saw a dress I liked the other day, and I'm going back for a second look. I may have some fittings done if I decide to buy it."

Mrs. Smithers nodded. "You'll be back for dinner?"

"Yes," Linda said. "I'll only be gone for a few hours."

Tony Lamson's shop on Rodeo Drive was wedged between a jewelry shop and a leather goods store. A ruffled red dress covered the mannequin in the window and Tony Lamson's name was written on the door in flowing gold script. Linda stopped in front of the shop and handed her keys to the parking attendant. A uniformed doorman opened the heavy brass door and when she walked into the salon an immaculately groomed blonde with the slow, seductive gait of a high-fashion model glided toward her.

"May I help you?"

"I'm Linda Brown. Steve Douglas arranged for me to see Mr. Lamson today."

The sophisticated woman nodded. "Ah, yes, I made that appointment myself. Mr. Lamson is with another client, but I'll let him know you're here." She disappeared through the curtained archway.

Linda seated herself on one of the gilded French chairs and began leafing through a fashion magazine. A door opened and her heart froze in mid-beat as she sniffed the flowery perfume and heard the tinkling falsetto of artificial laughter. Then, confirming Linda's worst speculations, Monique drifted through the arch.

Her eyes widened when she saw Linda. "Darling, how nice

to see you. I didn't know you had discovered dear Tony. How fortunate for you. His gowns have a way of helping even problem figures. Who told you about him?" Her forced smile held as much welcome as a rattler's.

Linda smiled back at her. She had the distinct impression that hers was one of the problem figures that needed Tony's expertise. But before she could answer, the statuesque receptionist spoke up. "Miss Brown was sent in by Mr. Douglas of Karizma Records. He asked us to design a very special gown for her; money is no object."

For the first time since Linda had met her Monique's face registered a genuine emotion. She had been too shocked to hide her reaction. *"Miss Brown* . . . really . . . sent in by Mr. Douglas . . . indeed. My dear, I had no idea that Steve Douglas was buying your clothes. That's a step up from the beach-boy crowd, isn't it? I don't imagine our mutual friend is aware of this?"

Linda gritted her teeth and barely managed a reply. "No."

By now Monique had recovered. She shrugged and threw up her hands in a typically theatrical gesture. "No matter . . . no need to worry . . . my lips are sealed. Your little arrangement with Steve only sweetens our agreement, so in the end, everyone will get what—or should I say *who?*—they want." Tossing back her head, she laughed and slithered out the door.

Linda's insides knotted painfully. First the Stew Pot and now here. Why did Monique have to be everywhere? She closed her eyes. Her guardian angel was definitely on strike; everything that could possibly go wrong was doing so. Now Monique's hold on her was even stronger. What would happen if Monique told Jason? How could she ever explain things to him? He'd never believe anything she told him. And what *could* she tell him? Monique would say she was having an affair with Steve, and if she denied that she would have to tell him that she was working so she could earn the money to take Andy away from him. Which was worse? There was no answer. She was trying to muddle through her misery when a tall, slender man in a black turtle-neck sweater and tight-fitting black trousers came through the arch.

"Miss Brown . . . so good to meet you; I'm Tony Lamson. Come inside and let's see what we can do for you. I know what the rest of the group is wearing, so I should be able to design the perfect outfit for you." He took her to the center of a thickly carpeted room, made her stand on a small marble platform and aimed a spotlight directly on her. Taking a drawing pad and pencil, he began sketching rapidly. "This is going to be easy. You have the perfect figure and coloring for my designs. I wish I could say the same for all my clients."

So much for Monique's estimate of her problems. Linda blushed and mumbled, "Thanks." She felt more like a department-store dummy than a flesh-and-blood woman. There was something unreal about the whole situation, and if it weren't for the Sapphires she would have run from the store. She had never minded being in the spotlight when she was singing, but then the audience was listening to her music, not just staring at her body. She had to fight down an urge to hunch her shoulders and cross her arms over her chest protectively.

At last Tony switched off the light and motioned Linda to a chair at the side of the room. "You've been an angel, standing so quietly like that. I was able to complete the entire design. Now I'd like your opinion before I have someone take your measurements."

Linda studied the figure on the sketch pad. The gown was far more daring than anything she had ever worn before. Cut low in the back, it fastened toga-like on one shoulder before flowing to the ankles in a full cascade of undulating pleats. It was the type of dress Monique usually wore, but Linda thought it might be too glamorous for her. "It's beautiful, but I've never worn anything like it before. It might be too . . ."

Tony waved his hands disdainfully. "Nonsense, I designed it especially for you. We'll do it in black velvet with an overlay of sequins and it will complement the men's outfits perfectly."

Linda stood up to leave. "If you're sure," she said doubtfully.

"I'm sure." Tony closed the sketch pad.

"When will it be ready?"

Tony thought for a moment. "Steve put a rush on this; I'll get on it right away. It's a bad time, too; every woman in town wants a new outfit for the Academy Awards. But Steve is one of my best clients." He smiled. "It should be ready for a fitting next week, maybe sooner. I'll call Steve and let him know."

Chapter Nine

Although the Sapphires had taken some time off, Jason had not. He was so busy at work that the only contact Linda had with him was on the telephone. She answered it one morning, expecting it to be Jason, and was surprised to hear Cindy Stone's voice on the other end.

"I'm glad I found you home. How have you been?"

"Just fine. And you?"

"Great. I thought we'd get together today. What do you have planned for the afternoon?"

"Nothing much."

"How about a game of tennis? Jason has one of the best courts in town. Have you tried it yet?"

"No, but I've seen it. I'd enjoy playing, but I have to warn you, I haven't been near a court since high school."

Cindy laughed. "That's better than me; I never even played in high school. I started lessons two years ago and my coordination leaves a lot to be desired."

"Fine," Linda said. "We seem ideally matched. How soon can you be here?"

Cindy hesitated for a moment. "I usually don't eat before I play, but I'm starving. Just give me a few minutes to grab a sandwich and change into my outfit."

"Look, I haven't played tennis in so long that I won't be able to do much more than lob a few balls over the net. We're not going to be racing around the court, so we don't have to worry about what we eat. Just change and come over; we can have that sandwich together."

"Super," Cindy said. "I'll be there in fifteen minutes."

Linda didn't have a tennis outfit, so she put on a pair of

shorts and a tee shirt. Mrs. Smithers was in the kitchen when Linda told her that she had invited Cindy for lunch. "Nothing special," she said. "Just some sandwiches. I can make them myself."

"I'll take care of it," Mrs. Smithers said. "It's no trouble at all."

By the time Cindy rang the bell the glass table on the terrace had been set for lunch. Instead of making the sandwiches Linda had suggested Mrs. Smithers had scooped out the insides of two large tomatoes, filled them with freshly made shrimp salad and set them on beds of lettuce and melon balls. Fresh rolls, butter and a large pitcher of iced tea were also on the table.

"You've done it again," Cindy said, smiling at Mrs. Smithers.

Mrs. Smithers smiled back. "How are you, Mrs. Stone?"

"Fine, thank you. I see you still make the tastiest lunches in town. You know, Linda, Mrs. Smithers is Jason's secret weapon. Her cooking is the reason his dinner parties are so popular. I've been trying to steal her away from him for years, but she won't even listen to me."

"Oh, go on with you," Mrs. Smithers said, but her face glowed as she returned to the kitchen.

Cindy sat down, lifted a piece of melon to her lips and made a face of pure delight. "This is so much better than the grilled cheese I was planning on." She looked at Linda, who was quietly picking at her food. "You look tired, Linda. Is something wrong? Maybe you ought to make an appointment with Ken. You never did get your checkup, did you?"

Linda shook her head. "I'm fine. I've just been busy running around, and this excitement is more than I'm used to. I'll be better once things have quieted down."

Cindy took a forkful of shrimp salad and grinned. "I'm afraid things won't be quiet for some time. The Academy Awards are being presented in two weeks, and that's the high point of the L.A. social season. It's a public acknowledgment of a job well done, a chance for performers to pat each other on the back and an excuse to throw the most lavish parties this town has ever seen. The winners have their little golden

Oscars to keep them company, but even the losers get a chance to party it up, and nobody stays miserable for long because there's always next year. Have you gotten your dress yet? There are a lot of people you haven't met, and this is just the occasion to knock their eyes out."

Linda put down her fork and shook her head. "Jason never mentioned it. I don't even know if I'm going."

"Nonsense, he goes every year. He has to; it's expected of him. In fact, we're going as his guests."

Linda shook her head. There was nothing she could say, no way she could explain that Jason had married her because of Andy, not because he loved her and wanted to be with her, that despite his efforts to make her a part of his life he would always think of her as a possession, never a companion. That was something she could never admit to Cindy or anyone else. It was too humiliating.

Obviously Cindy and Ken had a good marriage, one based on mutual love and sharing, so Cindy wouldn't understand the kind of marriage she and Jason had. Jason was probably going to attend the Awards presentation as well as the parties afterward, but despite all that he had said about always wanting to be with her, this was one time when his plans apparently didn't include his wife. She remembered seeing Monique at Tony Lamson's salon and visualized the glamorous star in one of his creations. She would look more beautiful than ever, and she was Jason's hottest new star. Was he planning on taking Monique to the Awards? Would he say it was for business reasons? The subject was too painful for Linda to think about, let alone discuss, even with someone as compassionate as Cindy. She shrugged, then stood. "I still have to find a tennis racket. I'm sure Jason must have an extra one somewhere."

Cindy pushed back her chair and groaned. "We should have eaten after the game. I'm much too full to start running around the court, but come on, I know where Jason keeps some spare rackets. You can use one of those today, but you'll have to get your own right away; no one around here would be caught dead without a racket designed especially for them. It's a sort of status symbol."

Laughing, Linda followed Cindy. "I guess that lets me out. I've never been comfortable with status symbols."

Cindy raised an eyebrow and grinned. "Are you kidding? You're living with the greatest status symbol of them all. Aren't you aware of Jason's stature in the industry?"

Linda smiled wanly. "Of course, I know Jason is a very important man; I was thinking of objects, not people." If Cindy only knew how uncomfortable she was with Jason.

Cindy nodded. "I see what you mean. Sometimes it's hard to imagine how prominent someone is when you live with them so intimately. Some of Ken's patients idolize him; of course, they never see how tired and worn out he is after a day's work."

Cindy's words reminded Linda of how tired Jason had been the night when she had helped him up to bed, the night when he had needed her. But what had happened since then? He had gone to work without a word. Obviously he no longer needed her. She had been a fool to think that she could ever mean anything to Jason. When would she ever learn her lesson?

She was grateful that Cindy had suggested playing tennis. Maybe the game would take her mind off Jason.

They went to the guest house where Linda had found her bathing suit. A shelf in a walk-in closet held some tennis rackets as well as several unopened cans of tennis balls. She tested a few rackets for weight and finally settled on an aluminum one. Then she took a can of balls. "Do you feel up to a game?" she asked Cindy as they walked toward the court. "Or are you still under the influence of Mrs. Smithers' cooking?"

"Something mild," Cindy laughed. "Just enough to work off the food. I don't think I could keep up with a fast game."

"Don't worry," Linda said. "I couldn't play a fast game even if I hadn't eaten since yesterday. Let's just lob a few over the net. I need the practice."

The match was friendly, with neither woman exerting herself very much, and when the ball went out of bounds they just laughed and went after it slowly. They didn't make any back-breaking attempts to ace the ball or keep a volley going. After a while they even stopped keeping score.

Finally Cindy held up her hands. "I've had enough. Your coordination is great; you could be a first-rate tennis player. You really should start taking lessons. I'd be glad to speak to my instructor."

"I don't know about that," a deep voice said. "I've heard about these Beverly Hills tennis instructors." Jason was leaning against the fence, smiling down at them.

Linda's heart blossomed when she saw him. The well-cut lines of his dark blue suit only accented the vibrant masculinity which it covered, and the arrogant jut of his aquiline features was softened by his smile. He walked toward them, casually draped his arm around Linda's waist and bent to kiss the top of her head. He seemed so relaxed, so at ease, as if he really were a loving husband greeting an equally loving wife.

Linda wiped her damp hands on her shorts and smoothed back the stray blond hairs that had escaped from her headband. The soft wool of Jason's jacket rubbed against her arm and she remembered what he had said about wanting his wife to dress properly. She looked down at her cut-offs and tried to pull away from him, but his arm tightened, keeping her at his side. Although Linda had always said that she didn't want to be his possession, she couldn't deny how comforting it felt to be held in this possessive manner. She lifted her hand to his shoulder and let her body relax against his as they moved across the lawn. Cindy fell into step beside them.

"Tennis lessons, hmm?" Jason said, flexing his fingers and pulling her even closer. "I guess you've had your fill of window shopping."

"I don't know," Linda said. "Let me think about it. I've never been much of a tennis buff. I think I'm going to use the pool a lot more than the tennis court."

Jason smiled. "Well, they're both here for you to enjoy. Just let Cindy know if you want lessons. I understand Ken has paid that instructor of hers a small fortune."

"Hush up, Jason," Cindy said. "We can't all be naturally athletic." She nodded knowingly toward Linda. "He's the sort I hate . . . never takes a lesson and plays like a pro."

When they reached the house Linda invited Cindy in for some iced tea, but the other woman checked her watch and refused. "I have barely enough time to change before my daughter's ballet lesson. Unfortunately, she's just as uncoordinated as her mother." She opened her car door, then turned and pointed an accusing finger at Jason. "Jason, why haven't you told Linda about the Academy Awards? You know she'll need time to get a dress. It's probably too late already." She shook her head. "Sometimes you men are absolutely thoughtless." She slid behind the wheel and waved to them as she coasted down the driveway.

Jason looked at Linda. "Are you coming in? I'd like to get out of this suit."

Linda nodded. "I could do with a shower. I never realized a friendly game of tennis could be so exhausting. And Jason, I want to thank you for the car. It's beautiful."

"I'm glad you like it." Jason followed Linda into her room. "I'm sorry I forgot to mention the Awards to you. Will you be able to get an outfit on such short notice?"

"Look, Jason, don't feel you have to take me just because of what Cindy said. She doesn't really understand about us."

"What's wrong with you?" Jason asked, grasping her by the shoulders. "I'm not taking you because of anything Cindy said. I'm taking you because you're my wife and I want you there with me. Is that too hard for you to understand?"

"You know what I mean," Linda said, shaking her head. "I'm not that well-known. People won't be expecting me to be there, so if you'd be more comfortable with someone else, I'd understand." She lowered her eyes, not trusting herself to look into his.

His finger slipped beneath her chin and tilted her face toward his. "And just what is that supposed to mean? Who would I be more comfortable with? Surely you're not thinking of Monique? She's got *her* image to think about. She'll be coming with her leading man; they're both up for awards. So, although she'll be sitting near us, she'll have her own escort, and I, my dear, will be with you. The only reason I didn't tell you about the Awards is that I've been busy with other things.

You know how hard I've been working. You did tuck me into bed the other night, didn't you, or was that my imagination?"

"I'm sorry, Jason. I just don't want to interfere with any of your plans."

Jason's mouth lowered to meet hers and caught her lips in a feathery kiss. "How could that happen? Haven't you been listening at all? You and Andrew are the most important part of *all* my plans."

Linda's body tensed as his lips moved against the corner of her mouth. Jason ran his fingers down her spine as if he were trying to massage away the tension, then he smiled casually. "I think you'd better take your shower while we're still on friendly terms. Our quiet conversations have an uncanny way of turning into arguments." He chucked her under the chin and walked toward the adjoining door.

Linda stood where she was and watched him go. He went into his room, turned to look back at her, then left the door open just as she had done that night. A tide of pleasure swelled in Linda's heart and she smiled back at him. She knew that he had understood the gesture she had made and, by accepting it, had decided not to force her into anything and to let her determine the pace of their marriage. For the first time in their relationship he had made her feel like his equal. She hummed to herself as she turned on the shower.

Jason, looking totally relaxed in an open-necked white sport shirt and snug-fitting camel-colored trousers, was lying across her bed when she came out of the bathroom wearing only a short terrycloth robe. His brooding eyes followed her movements and she felt more uncomfortable under his scrutiny than she had been under Tony Lamson's. She stopped toweling her hair and looked at him.

"Is something wrong?"

"No, why should anything be wrong?"

"I don't know. Just the way you're watching me."

"I like watching you. I imagine most husbands watch their wives get dressed. Our living arrangements haven't given me many chances, so I'm enjoying this more than most." His voice softened. "Do you mind very much?"

Linda looked down at the towel and began pleating it

between her fingers. "No, I don't mind, not really." She was telling the truth because she had suddenly realized that it wasn't his watching her that was making her nervous, it was his attitude. She looked at the open door, then turned back to meet his expectant gaze. The next move was up to her; he was sitting on her bed, waiting. Suddenly, she wasn't so sure that she wanted to be the one to make the decision. Wouldn't it be easier to let Jason seduce her into his arms? Then he would have to bear the blame for anything that went wrong. She shook her head. She couldn't think that way ever again; if she did, Jason was right to call her a child.

"Linda." Jason lifted his hand and held it out to her.

She came to him and sat on the edge of the bed.

He bent toward her and took the towel. "Let me dry your hair." His voice was husky as he folded her hair into the towel. "Do you have any idea how soft this feels?" He dropped the towel and combed his fingers through the tendrils.

She tilted her head and looked up at him. "I just washed it."

"It felt soft the very first time I touched it. Do you remember?"

She nodded. He had compared it to strands of silk.

"Do you still hate me?" His thumbs stroked the sensitive area behind her ears.

She shook her head and didn't resist when he leaned forward and lowered her to the mattress.

"You know how I feel . . . what I want. But I won't force you. We've got too much at stake. We've got to make this work. Tell me you're willing. Tell me you want me, too."

Linda looked up at him. His features were as strained as they had been the first time he took her in his arms. But then she had been sure that he loved her; now she knew he didn't. The word he had used was "want." At first he had wanted her body; now he wanted both her body and the child that had come from it. His gaze was just as possessive as it had been the first time he looked at her, but no more loving.

But hadn't he been trying to change? Hadn't he just said that he wouldn't force her, that she had to want him before he would touch her? Was it too soon? If she gave in now, admitted that she no longer hated him, that the love she had felt was returning—had returned—would he treat her like a child? She was too afraid to take what he'd said as the truth; there *was* too much at stake. She needed to be sure; she needed more time.

She lifted her hands and, fighting down the urge to touch his face, pressed them against his chest. "Not yet, Jason, not yet."

His fingers left her hair and stroked the side of her cheeks. "But soon, Linda . . . soon?" His voice was husky with desire.

"Soon," she agreed. "Very soon."

Dipping his head, he pressed his lips lightly against hers. Then he sat up and, taking her hand in his, lifted her toward him. "You'd better get dressed."

Her legs were shaking as she walked to the closet. She had followed the dictates of her mind, but her body was disappointed. She sat on the vanity bench and began brushing the tangles out of her hair. Jason watched her from the bed.

"Will you be having dinner at home?" she asked, trying to ease the tension.

"Yes. I think I've finally gotten things under control. My lawyers can handle the rest."

Linda nodded, walked to the dressing area and changed into a lounging outfit. She was tying the belt on the clinging jersey top when she walked back into the room. Jason's eyes raked her body, taking in the low vee of the neckline and the soft, fluid lines of the trousers.

"I like what you're wearing. The blue is a perfect match for the sapphire shading of your eyes. You should always wear that color."

Linda turned away as he levered himself off the bed. An uncomfortable feeling was churning in the pit of her stomach. Jason's mention of her eyes had reminded her of her deceit; her deep blue eyes had been one of the reasons Steve had wanted her to join the Sapphires. She liked being part of the group, and singing was something she needed to do, but she knew Jason would never understand. She'd have to choose between Jason and her career, but she couldn't make that choice—not now. She had to get away; she didn't even want to think about it. "I'm going in to Andy. There's still some time before dinner and he'll probably be sleeping by the time we've finished." She opened the door and Jason came up behind her.

Mrs. Mason had just taken Andy out of his high chair and was preparing to take him upstairs when they walked into the kitchen. Jason reached for him. "Why don't you relax for a while, Mrs. Mason? Linda and I will watch him."

He went into the library and handed Andy to Linda, who had followed. "Would you like a cocktail before dinner?"

"White wine, thank you." She covered her eyes and started playing peek-a-boo with Andy. He giggled and pulled at her fingers.

Jason laughed and handed Linda her wine. It nearly tipped when Andy reached for it. Smiling, she held the glass out of reach and looked at Jason. "Now what do I do?" She felt as though she were doing a balancing act.

"You need some help," Jason said. "You just can't manage by yourself." He left his martini on the bar, walked to her side, put one arm over her shoulder and nestled Andy in the other. "That's better, now, isn't it? We need each other; isn't that what I've always said?" He pressed her closer to his side.

She trembled and leaned against him. His arms were a protective circle sheltering her and Andy. Suddenly she knew that this was what she wanted. But she wanted her singing, too. She wanted it all, Jason, Andy and the Sapphires. Turning toward Jason, she put one arm on his shoulder and the other around Andy. Jason closed his eyes and pressed his lips against her forehead. Warm contentment spread through Linda's body.

She pulled herself away when Kim and Mrs. Mason appeared in the doorway. Mrs. Mason took Andy, and Kim announced that dinner was ready.

Two tall, thin candles, surrounded by a bowl of white gardenias, flickered in the middle of the dining-room table. While they ate Jason told Linda how JMR Productions had been created when he, as A and R man for a larger company, had taken a chance on an unknown group of teenage singers. "Their first album hit the top of the charts almost immediately. I liked their sound, so I formed my own company and backed every other similar group I could get my hands on. I guess my success was due to intuition and luck."

"And hard work," Linda said, cutting into her prime rib.

"And hard work," Jason agreed. "But now I'm going to start taking things easy. I'm a family man; I have other things to think about." His eyes met hers across the table.

When they had finished their chocolate mousse Jason suggested that they have their coffee in the library. Kim put the tray on the table in front of the sofa and left, then Linda sat down and began pouring the coffee. Jason went to the stereo and put on a tape of the sound track from his latest movie. Then he sat beside her.

She handed him his cup, but he shook his head. "No coffee now, just you." He captured her hand and pulled her closer.

"The music is nice," she said, trying to hide her tension.

"You're nicer." His fingers moved beneath her hair and began stroking the back of her neck. "Don't tense up on me. I only want you near me. I only want to hold you."

"Jason, we said we needed more time, remember?" She was warning herself more than him.

"You said *you* needed more time. *I* haven't ever needed anything but you." His fingers feathered her neck and traced the plunging neckline of her tunic. "You're more beautiful than you were the first time I saw you. Then you were a girl, now you're a woman, the mother of my son."

"Oh, Jason." She sighed and turned her head into his shoulder. His heartbeat vibrated against the softness of her cheek. There were so many reasons why she should hate him, yet so many more reasons why she couldn't. As he had said, she was the mother of his child, and the feelings which had drawn her to him that very first night had never really died; they had merely slipped beneath the surface. Now they were back, stronger than ever. Succumbing to her emotions, she went limp and relaxed against the strength of his chest.

He cupped her chin and brought his lips to hers, kissing her tenderly at first, then with increasing intensity until the kiss had become a passionate demand. She was tired of thinking and finding excuses. All she knew was that she loved Jason and wanted to stay in his arms forever.

Supporting her with his arm, he shifted his body and gently pressed her down. His hand cupped her breast, then traced a line along the curve of her hip. His lips left hers, feathered her jaw and the pulsing vein in her neck, then lingered in the scented hollow between her breasts.

Arching her back, she combed her fingers through his hair and urged him even closer. For once her mind and her body both wanted the same things—Jason's love, Jason's touch.

He tensed, put his hands around her wrists and sat up. "This is much too public for what I have in mind." His voice was husky and uneven. He lifted her into his arms and started for the door.

She linked her arms around his neck and pressed her lips to his cheek, inhaling the spicy male scent of his after-shave lotion. Her body quivered in anticipation.

"You're driving me crazy," he said in a raw, husky voice.

Kim rounded the corner just as they stepped into the hallway. "Phone call, Mr. Reynolds. Miss Jenson said it was important."

Jason's arms tightened around Linda; then he sighed and bent to release her.

Linda tried to listen, but since she was only hearing Jason's half, she couldn't understand the conversation. Finally he slammed down the receiver.

"I'm sorry about this, Linda, but they need me at the office. There's been a snag in the negotiations. Their attorney found a few words he didn't like and now we have to rewrite the entire contract. Lawyers thrive on disputes; they hate it when things go smoothly. It's a wonder we ever get anything done with them around." He shook his head. "I'll be back as soon as I can." He kissed her on the cheek and walked into the entryway, calling for Kim.

Linda's heart dropped as she watched him leave. She could tell that now he was thinking about business and had completely forgotten about her. She went back to the library and sipped her coffee absently, but the soft music no longer offered her any relaxation; the library seemed cold and lonely without Jason. She went upstairs, checked on Andy and prepared for bed.

She spent two hours brushing her hair, filing her nails and thumbing through magazines, but still Jason hadn't returned. Although he had said he would be back as soon as possible, he hadn't actually asked her to wait up for him; that was something she had decided on for herself. Sighing, she picked up another magazine and slipped into bed, leaving the light on so Jason would know she was up.

Despite her best efforts, exhaustion overcame her and she fell asleep. When she awoke it was morning and her light was still on. She got out of bed and walked into Jason's room. The neatly made bed looked as if it hadn't been slept in. He must have worked through the night. Linda remembered how tired he had been the night that seemed, in retrospect, to have marked a turning point in their relationship, and she found herself worrying about him. This is certainly a change, she told herself. Only a short while ago she had been wishing he'd be struck by lightning and disappear from the face of the earth; now she was brooding about the dark circles under his eyes. She shook her head and sighed. Her feelings about Jason had never been easy to explain.

As soon as she had showered and dressed she went downstairs to ask about him. Mrs. Smithers told her that he had spent the night at the office and had sent Kim home for a change of clothes. "Don't worry," she told Linda. "This isn't the first time he's done that. There's a bath off his private office, and his couch can convert to a bed."

But I was here waiting for him, Linda thought. Apparently Jason's work still came first. She grimaced and checked her watch. Work. She had almost forgotten her job. The Sapphires were recording today. "I don't have time for breakfast," she told Mrs. Smithers, then, looping her bag over her shoulder, she headed out the door.

Now, more than ever, she felt uneasy about singing with the Sapphires. The possibility of improving her relationship with Jason made her feel guilty about deceiving him, but she didn't know how to stop. She was sure that he wouldn't understand what she had done, and his anger might shatter the flimsy foundation of their new relationship. If only they could spend some time together she might be able to make him understand, but if he kept working at his usual pace she doubted that the chance would ever come.

She had just parked her car and was walking into the building when Steve Douglas fell into step beside her. He looked as tired as Jason had been looking lately.

"Still working hard?" she asked.

"It's nearly sewed up." He combed his fingers through his hair. "How are you doing?"

"Fine." She hesitated for a moment. "Steve, I need a special dress in a hurry. Could I borrow the one Tony's making? It would save me a hassle."

Steve nodded. "Sure. It's your dress. Just don't ruin it before we take the pictures."

"Thanks, I'll be careful." She smiled and looked at him. "You look exhausted."

He nodded. "This deal got out of hand. I've been working on it all night. But I think it's finally straightened out." He waved as Linda left the elevator for the recording studio. "I'll tell you all about it later."

Linda waved to the engineers in the control booth and went down to the recording floor. The rest of the Sapphires were already there, tuning up their instruments.

"We're ready to start," Bill said. "It may be different from what you're used to. We each record separately, then the others join in as they listen to the earlier recordings. I'll go first to establish the beat," he said, and sat down at the snare drum. "You do your lyrics and Terry and Jeff can bring up the rear."

The red silence light flashed on and Linda adjusted her earphones as Bill began recording his segment of the song. In a short while the engineer played back his version while Linda listened on her earphones and added her accompaniment to the parts he had already recorded. After the engineer had mixed the two versions, he played the new tapes back while Bill and Jeff sang their rendition of the melody. Then the engineer took over again to regulate the modulation and assemble the entire recording.

"Come on," Jeff said. "Let's have some coffee while they work on the mix. We'll hear it when they've finished." Linda looked at the clock and was amazed to see that the process, with its numerous retakes and delays while someone adjusted something, had taken hours.

They sat and talked until finally the engineer signaled from the control booth, telling them that he had done the final mix and was ready to cut the master disc. Linda looked quizzically at Bill.

He smiled indulgently. "I can see we're going to have to educate you in the jargon of the record industry. The master disc is the final cut of the record, a combination of all the recordings with the adjustments done by the sound engineers. It's the metal recording from which all the plastic discs are made."

Linda smiled as the vibrant sounds of her song filled the studio. All their efforts had been blended into an unusually attractive musical arrangement.

When the song was finished Jeff nodded with satisfaction. "Perfect, just perfect." He patted Linda's shoulder and called to the engineer, "That's the one."

"That sounds good. I think we have a hit if we market it right," Steve said from the control booth. He looked slightly more rested. "We'll release it as a single. I'll invite a couple of disc jockeys to lunch and give them some preview copies. If we can get them to start spinning it now, we'll have the kids clamoring for it before it even hits the racks. Now, why don't you all come up to my office? There's something I have to tell you."

"Coffee?" Steve offered after they walked into his office.

"Not me," Bill said. "I just want to get out of here and head for the beach. I'm ready for a good two-week vacation."

Steve smiled. "I know you creative artists aren't interested in mundane business transactions, but since this may affect sales, I thought you should be among the first to know. Karizma Records has been engaged in merger negotiations with JMR Industries. They're into movies and television, and they need someone to control their record division. They like our sound, and it's an excellent opportunity for us. We'll have the worldwide distribution facilities of JMR Industries, and they've promised to retain our entire staff and give us almost complete control over the record division. Well, say something. What do you think?"

"Sounds good," Jeff said. "I don't care who handles the paper work as long as they sell my records and don't hassle me by trying to tell me how to sing."

The other men nodded. Only Linda sat silently, too shocked to say anything. Steve looked at her expectantly.

"It doesn't make any difference to me," she said, suddenly feeling weak and nauseated.

Steve stared at her for a moment, then snapped his fingers as if he had suddenly remembered something. "Tony Lamson called; he wants you to stop by for a fitting." He looked at his watch. "You'd better get there right away."

Linda welcomed the excuse to leave. She needed some time alone, time to think about what Steve had just said. If Karizma Records became a subsidiary of JMR Industries she would be working for Jason. It would be impossible to keep her involvement with the Sapphires from him and he would have the power to control her career. She was sure he would stop her from recording and might even blacklist the entire group. What a terrible thing to happen to the others after they had worked so hard and were finally on the brink of success. The best thing she could do for the Sapphires would be to leave the group and let them get another female singer. Luckily she had never given Steve her telephone number or address, so he wouldn't be able to trace her. Now, if Monique would just keep quiet about what she knew, things might work out.

Linda parked the car behind Tony Lamson's salon and thought about the dress. It was probably wrong to keep it if she wasn't going to be part of the group, but she needed it for the Academy Awards. And she wasn't going to let Steve pay for it, so she wasn't being totally dishonest. How much simpler things would be if only she hadn't tried to deceive

Jason. More than anything, she wanted to be part of the family he kept talking about. She wanted to be with him and Andy. She wanted to have more children, Jason's children; she wanted that more than singing, more than anything. Why had it taken her so long to realize that? Talk about tangled webs of deception, she thought, shaking her head disconsolately and walking into the shop.

Tony Lamson was expecting her and she was immediately shown to a dressing room. The receptionist brought in a beautiful black velvet gown which was an almost exact replica of the sketch Tony had made the other day. Swirls of sequins made the dress heavy and she appreciated the receptionist's help as she slipped it over her shoulders and turned to have it zipped up.

Tony Lamson was slumped in a white and gold bergère chair when she walked out. His close-fitting black turtle-neck outfit was a duplicate of the one he had been wearing the other day, and Linda assumed that it was his working uniform. When he saw her he stood and motioned her toward the platform in the center of the room. His face was noncommittal as he circled her, stroking his chin pensively.

Finally he spoke. "Perfect, it's perfect. I don't have to change a thing. There's not even any pinning to be done. You can take it home right now, just as soon as we've pressed it."

Linda took off the gown and waited in the privacy of her dressing room. She had no desire to go outside, where she might run into Monique again. She got into her own clothes and stretched out on the chaise longue. When she told Tony that she was tired and preferred to wait in the dressing room he offered to have the dress delivered. But she said she'd wait; she didn't want to give him her address. When the dress was ready and she asked Tony for the bill he replied that he would send it to Steve. He told her not to worry because Karizma Records was paying for it, but Linda insisted and eventually won out.

When the receptionist showed her the bill she couldn't believe it. She didn't know how she could possibly ask Jason to pay such an exorbitant sum, but she would feel worse about letting Steve foot the bill now that she had to leave the

Sapphires. She watched Tony's assistant arrange the gown in her car, then she drove silently home, her thoughts so hopelessly muddled that she couldn't even think about solving her problems.

When she got home Jason was on the lawn playing with Andy. Kim had hung a baby swing from a branch of a large mimosa tree; Andy was sitting in the canvas seat and Jason was pushing him gently. Leaving the dress in the car she went around back to join them. Andy held out his arms and Jason kissed her on the cheek.

"Been window shopping again?" Jason asked.

Linda smiled with mock pride. "As a matter of fact, I bought something . . . a dress for the Academy Awards. When you see the bill, though, you'll wish I *had* been window shopping."

Jason laughed and lifted Andy out of the swing. "I hope I haven't created a monster. You're not going to be like Barbara and spend all your time shopping, are you?"

Linda fell into step beside him as he walked to the house. "No, I think this dress completes my wardrobe. From now on I'll probably be spending most of my time around here. Andy's more fun than shopping any day."

Chuckling, Jason lifted Andy to his shoulders. "You won't get any argument from me on that score."

Andy laughed as Jason raced up the stairs carrying the baby on his back. Hot tears welled in Linda's eyes when she thought about how devoted Jason was to his son. It was hard to believe that a man who had such a cold reputation in business could be so warm and loving to his child. But how would he react to her deception, Linda wondered? Would he be the loving, trusting father or the deceived entrepreneur? Somehow Linda felt it would be the latter. Although her feelings for him were now clearly defined—she loved him, without a doubt—she still wasn't sure how he felt about her. Did he care about her as a person, or did he think of her only as Andy's mother? She didn't know. Jason loved his son so much that there wasn't anything he wouldn't do for him, including marrying her. Linda wondered if her love for Andy was just as strong, because if you loved someone, you had to do what was best for them, even if by doing so you made yourself miserable.

Now that she had left the Sapphires she knew that Andy would have to stay with his father—no matter what happened. She couldn't deprive him of all the material advantages Jason could offer, especially since she knew that he'd also have a surplus of love. She realized that she hadn't wanted to take Andy away for his own good; she had been doing it for herself—to get back at Jason, to punish him for hurting her. But she couldn't deceive herself anymore, and if Jason decided to end their marriage, she would walk away—alone.

Jason was called away on business that night and for the rest of the week, as well. Linda barely saw him, as he seemed to be in constant demand at his office. On the one occasion when she did get more than two minutes with him, he apologized and promised her a family vacation in Hawaii as soon as things quieted down. Linda couldn't understand why he was so busy, since Steve had said the deal with Karizma was finalized. But then, the Karizma merger probably wasn't the only business transaction on Jason's mind; JMR Industries was a huge conglomerate.

The night of the Academy Awards arrived, and as Linda began dressing, her excitement became tinged with apprehension. Jason still hadn't come home, but Miss Jenson had called earlier to say that, although he was delayed at the office, Linda should be ready to leave by five. She glanced into Jason's room before taking her shower and saw that Kim had laid out his evening suit. Apparently he was still planning on taking her to the Awards presentations. She smiled as she closed the door and turned on the shower.

She had toweled herself dry and had slipped into her lacy undergarments when she heard Kim's and Jason's voices coming through the closed door of the adjoining room. She didn't want Jason to have to wait for her, so, after applying a thin coat of cheek blusher and dusting her face lightly with translucent powder, she highlighted her blue eyes and put on some pale pink lip gloss. She pulled her long blond hair back and curled it into a softly shimmering cascade, giving her the profile of a beautiful Grecian goddess.

She slipped into the dress and was unsuccessfully trying to manipulate the back zipper when the adjoining door opened and Jason came in. Sighing, she straightened out of her uncomfortable position. "Am I glad to see you. I'll never be able to do this alone."

Jason looked at her just as he had that first time. His eyes met hers and held them as he walked toward her. An uncontrollable shiver of desire ran through her body and she turned her back to him slowly, her fingers still clutching nervously at the edges of her dress.

Stopping behind her, he rested his hands on her shoulders and slid them forward, letting his long fingers drop to the soft beginnings of her breasts. Aching ecstasy quivered in her abdomen and spread through her body. She released her dress, turned to him and put her arms around his neck. His hands moved up, his palms framing her face and raising her lips to his. She stepped closer, slowly rotating her hips as she tried to mold her pliant body against the hardening strength of his.

Dragging his lips from hers, he dropped them to the curve of her shoulder and lifted her into his arms. Leaning back, she arched her neck and willed his lips to move even lower. He placed her on the bed and stared down at her.

"We don't have to go, you know; there are more important things than award dinners." His eyes caressed her face and lingered at the rising swell of her breasts.

She was too choked by emotion to answer, but her silent love reached out to him, telling him that his touch meant more than anything. They remained mute, eyes fastened on each other, lost in a private world that held the promise of joy to come. Jason's fingers combed through her hair, fanning it out on the pillow. "Linda, I . . ." The harsh, rasping sound of a car's motor sounded on the driveway; Kim was waiting for them.

Linda blinked as if awakening from a dream. She ran her moist tongue over her dry lips. "We'd better be leaving. Everyone expects you, Jason; you have to be there."

She looked at him, half hoping he would say she was wrong, that they could spend the evening here, locked in each other's arms, but he groaned and lifted himself off the bed.

"You're probably right; we should be there. It's only a few hours, and we do have the rest of our lives together." He smiled at her. "I'll go in to Andrew and let Mrs. Mason help you finish dressing. I'm afraid I'd be useless, since it's apparent that my inclinations lie in the opposite direction."

Mrs. Mason zipped up the dress and watched while Linda fixed her makeup and repinned the hair that Jason's fingers had loosened. After spraying some perfume at her pulse points, she took the small black evening bag Mrs. Mason held out to her.

The older woman smiled her approval. "Who would ever recognize you as the girl in jeans from Laguna Beach? You look like a movie star."

"Thank you," Linda said, hugging her.

"Linda, are you coming?" Jason called.

"I'll be right there." She joined him in the nursery and kissed Andy goodnight. Then she and Jason went downstairs together.

When they reached the entryway he motioned for her to wait, then took a beautiful sable coat from the hall closet. "A very special present for a very special lady . . . my wife." He slipped the coat around her and stood behind her, holding onto her shoulders as if he couldn't bear to let her go.

Linda covered his hands with hers. "It's beautiful, Jason." She turned to look at him. "Thank you, thank you for everything."

He looked at her for a moment, then, dragging his eyes away, he grasped her hand and pulled her toward the door. "If you keep looking at me like that we're going to head right back up that stairway and the Academy Awards will have to proceed without us."

A warm flush of pleasure flooded Linda's body as Jason's unhappy voice indicated how he would rather spend the evening, but she remembered what he had said about spending the rest of their lives together and smiled in anticipation as they went out to the car.

Chapter Ten

The bright arc lights made the dancing waters of the fountains in front of the Music Center look like a shimmering cascade of diamonds as Kim pulled the Mercedes into the long line of expensive cars that were waiting to discharge their passengers. Hordes of reporters and photographers surrounded the cars, hoping for a celebrity interview, while policemen and wooden barricades separated a crowd of screaming fans from the movie idols they had come to see.

A uniformed doorman opened her door and Jason, who had turned the car over to an attendant, gave Linda his hand as she got out of the car. Waving to the reporters, he smiled and bent to whisper in her ear. "Everyone is wondering who you are. They think you're some beautiful new starlet. Now, don't get upset tomorrow morning when you read in the newspapers that I was seen at the Academy Awards with a stunning blonde. Just remember they're talking about you and don't start storming at me." He pulled her closer to his side, his large hand exerting a gentle pressure against her narrow waist.

Linda's body went boneless as she molded herself to the length of his. She loved being with him and being held by him; she never wanted to lose this feeling of contentment. She turned her head to look at Jason. How did he feel about her? His face was an expressionless mask and she couldn't tell. Twisting her hips slightly, she edged closer to him; he smiled down at her and pressed his fingers into her waist. Joy blossomed in her heart. He still wanted her and, given enough time, that desire might turn to love. She snuggled closer. Right now Jason's love meant more to her than anything except Andy. But weren't they the same? Wasn't Andy the concrete expression of Jason's love? She wanted to think so. Sighing, she rested her head on Jason's shoulder.

They walked through the wide doors of the Dorothy Chandler Pavilion, one of the three buildings comprising the Music Center and the site of the Awards ceremony, and were immediately bathed in the soft light of the huge crystal chandeliers. An usher guided them down the aisle to their seats, and Linda was happy to see that Ken and Cindy Stone were already there.

Ken stood as she approached, lifting his eyebrow and raking her body with a mockingly lecherous glare. "Can this be the same girl I treated for exhaustion six weeks ago? I'll bet I never get invited into her bedroom again."

Cindy poked him playfully in the ribs. "Sit down, Ken, before Jason takes you seriously."

"If I took him seriously he'd have to find a new tennis partner," Jason said. "But just to be on the safe side, Linda will see you at your office from now on, with that formidable nurse of yours looking on."

Everyone laughed and Cindy bent to speak to Linda. "Where did you get that fabulous dress? And the coat? You certainly did all right for someone who had no idea she was going to be here tonight. If that's what you get on the spur of the moment I'd love to see what you can do when you really have the time to shop."

Linda didn't want to lie and she couldn't tell the truth, so she just smiled as Jason explained, "I guess all her window shopping paid off. I'll probably have to ground her when I get the bill for this gown, but she looks so beautiful that I'll be happy to pay whatever it costs." He smiled. "As for the coat, that's a gift from an admiring husband."

Linda flushed pleasurably and Jason put his hand around her shoulder, drawing her close to him once more. His warm breath teased her cheek as he whispered into her ear. "You'll have to stop blushing every time I tell you how beautiful you are because I intend to make complimenting you a lifelong occupation."

Linda didn't answer; she was too busy basking in the warmth of his embrace. Her body responded to his touch just as it had on that very first night and his caressing hands rekindled the fires smoldering deep within her body. She snuggled closer, rubbing her cheek against the soft wool of his jacket and basking in the spicy scent of his cologne. A combined feeling of security and love made her look up at him. She was in a state of enchantment and loved him so much that she wanted to surround herself with the touch, scent and sight of him.

The magic of the moment was shattered when Jason rose to greet Monique and her escort, whom Linda recognized as the handsome leading man she had seen with Monique at the restaurant in Santa Monica. But she was probably the only one in the theater who had noticed Monique's escort; everyone else was staring at Monique. Her strapless white beaded gown was completely slit up one side to reveal one shapely leg from ankle to thigh. Her long, blond hair was a mass of wild curls and diamonds sparkled at her fingers, wrists, ears and neck. Tossing her ermine boa over the back of her seat, she waved to some friends, then settled herself with as much ceremony as she could possibly manage.

Linda looked at Monique and drew closer to Jason. She just couldn't bear to lose him, not now, not when she knew how desperately she loved him. Yet Monique was so beautiful; what had Cindy said? How could Jason or any man resist her? Suddenly Tony Lamson's black-sequined gown seemed about as elegant as a pair of tattered jeans. There were some things that even a designer gown couldn't do, and Linda felt that she would never have that special charisma that would always make Monique the star attraction.

The seats around them filled quickly with other executives from JMR Industries and Linda found herself dutifully listening while Monique held court. The only thing that finally silenced her was the announcement that the award presentations were about to begin. Glancing at Monique, Linda realized that the beautiful blonde was nervous; she had been nominated for an award as the best supporting actress.

The theater lights dimmed and the stage lights flashed on. A warm feeling of camaraderie swept through the hall when the name of each recipient was announced, because everyone there realized the years of hard work that had gone into each award-winning performance. Despite her personal feelings about the woman, Linda clapped enthusiastically when the spotlight shifted toward them and Monique stepped forward to receive her golden Oscar. She made the customary acceptance speech, then returned to plant a passionate kiss on Jason's lips. It was definitely more intimate than the brief peck a grateful star normally bestowed on the head of her studio, and Linda's heart shriveled in her breast when she realized that the picture in the paper the next morning would not be of Jason and her, but rather of Jason and Monique. When Jason's arms opened to return the embrace Linda lowered her eyes. She couldn't bear the sight of Jason caressing another woman; it was just too painful.

She sat through the remainder of the ceremonies in a fog of unrelieved depression. Monique was chatting with Jason, her hands clutching at his arms and shoulders; they both seemed to have forgotten that Linda existed. It was apparent that Monique had only come to the Awards with her leading man for publicity purposes; she really wanted to be with Jason. And Jason was doing absolutely nothing to rebuff her advances. On the contrary, he was obviously enjoying them. Linda was more miserable than she had ever been.

Finally the presentations were over. Linda couldn't even remember who had won the major awards. She just wanted to go home, to be alone and cry. How could she have been foolish enough to think that Jason really cared for her? Why couldn't she understand that he was only being nice to her so he could coax her into becoming a complacent wife who would stay meekly at home having his babies while he pursued more pleasurable interests—interests like Monique?

She was muddling through this melancholy reverie when her shoulder was gripped viciously from behind. She swung around and found herself staring into Steven Douglas' angry face. One whiff of his breath told her that he'd been drinking.

"So this is Tony Lamson's gown . . . the one I'm paying for. At least let me see what I've bought. You really took me for a ride, with that talk about your husband not understanding. Mr. Brown indeed." He looked at Jason. "All the time we were negotiating you had your little spy right in my nest. Does she play up to all your takeovers, or was I something special?"

Everyone was shocked into silence. Jason made a fist and lunged toward Steve, but Ken Stone and Monique's escort held him back. Other people who were within hearing distance watched with interest and newspaper photographers began snapping pictures. Linda lifted her eyes to Jason's and encountered a stare of utter revulsion. A knife plunged through her battered heart; she might have withstood his indifference, but she could never live with his hatred.

"I assume you have an explanation for this?" His voice cut through her as he shrugged free of Ken's imprisoning grip. "Just what does it all mean? No wonder you never bought anything on your little shopping expeditions. You were never near a store, were you? How many other men have there been besides Douglas?"

Linda shook her head in disbelief. This couldn't be happening, not in front of all these people. Jason loomed above her, irrational loathing showing clearly on his face. Fear united with shame as Linda backed away from him. She pressed her fist against her mouth and charged wildly out of the theater, not caring where she ran, only seeking an escape from Jason's condemning eyes.

The front of the theater was crowded with people waiting for their limousines and tears clouded Linda's vision as she edged her way aimlessly through the throng. She had no idea where she was going or how she would get there; she only knew she had to keep moving, putting more and more distance between herself and Jason. Recklessly she fled down the steps of the Music Center and onto the pavement of the deserted street. The magic of the evening was behind her in more ways than one, for upon leaving the glitter of the Music Center she had entered the cold reality of downtown Los

Angeles. Hesitantly, she stood on the corner, feeling like Cinderella after the clock had struck twelve. She had left her fur coat in the theater and was rubbing her hands over her arms to keep from shivering when suddenly a long, black Rolls-Royce pulled to a halt near the curb beside her.

As she backed away, frightened and not knowing what to expect, an elderly gray-haired lady lowered the window. "Are you in trouble? May I offer you a ride?"

Linda recognized the voice of an aging actress, a woman so famous that she was known as the dowager queen of the film industry. Linda hesitated for a moment, then nodded her head. "I'd be most appreciative."

The uniformed chauffeur opened the door and Linda settled herself beside the still beautiful woman.

"Now, my dear, where can we take you?"

"I'm not sure," Linda said, shaking her head. "A hotel, I think, but I don't really know of any."

The actress looked quizzically at Linda, then shrugged in a gesture which seemed to say that nothing surprised her anymore. "Well, my dear, since you need a hotel and don't know of any, why not come to mine for the evening? You can make more definite plans in the morning."

They headed back to Beverly Hills, moving along Sunset Boulevard until the chauffeur turned into a quiet, tree-lined street and drove through the wrought-iron gates of a picturesque estate that seemed more like an old French château than a modern California hotel. Graceful white swans drifted lazily among the lily-pads in the softly illuminated pond and the tensions of the outside world seemed to be banished from this secluded fairyland. The car stopped in front of a small pink cottage and the chauffeur helped the movie star get out.

"I'll be leaving now. My chauffeur will take you to the lobby, where you can arrange for a room. I'll speak with you in the morning. Problems have a way of solving themselves once we've had a good night's sleep." Majestically, she walked to her cottage.

Linda sat back in her seat and watched the chauffeur help the actress up the dimly lit path. She shook her head disconsolately and sighed; if only her problems could be solved by morning. But that was wishful thinking; her deception had created a problem that no amount of time could solve. Her thoughts twisted hopelessly and she sat numbly while the chauffeur drove to the hotel's main building.

Her reception at the registration desk was extremely cold and Linda wasn't sure that even the aging movie star's recommendation would get her a room in this hotel. Thank heavens Jason had given her some money the other day and she still had it in her wallet. At least she'd be able to pay for her night's lodging. When she gave her name as Linda Brown the desk clerk looked at her arrogantly and made some cursory checks through his files as if he were searching for her name. Naturally she wasn't listed and his look became more disdainful, indicating that she definitely didn't belong in this magnificent structure. When he learned that she had no luggage he practically sputtered in disgust.

She needed a room desperately and it was all too obvious that the desk clerk wouldn't even give Linda Brown a chair in the lobby. She searched for a famous name, one that he would recognize and respect. "Linda Brown is my professional name," she explained. "I'm married to Jason Reynolds."

The clerk eyed her quizzically; she could see that he hadn't decided whether to believe her. Suddenly he shrugged and again began checking through his file of white, blue and pink cards.

"Ah, here it is, Jason Reynolds." He pulled out a pink card. After studying the card for a few moments he rang for a bellhop and had her shown to a bungalow pleasantly isolated beneath some towering palm trees.

Linda admired the gracious elegance of the cottage after the bellhop had gone. The room was decorated entirely in delicately gilded French antiques. All the furniture was upholstered in a soft shade of blue that matched the pastel hue of the plush carpeting. Although the structure was old Linda saw that no expense had been spared to keep it up as luxuriously as when it had first been built. She wandered around the rooms, checking the well-stocked bar, marveling at the fresh floral arrangements and wondering how the ice and food snacks had been delivered so quickly. They must have been carried over while she was waiting for the bellhop.

This would be a marvelous place for a vacation, an ideal lovers' hideaway. Lovers . . . Instantly her thoughts centered on Jason. He had offered her the chance to be his wife, but she had rejected him, insisting that they had a relationship only because they were Andy's parents. Then, to make matters worse, she had taken the job with the Sapphires—done it behind his back. That she had cheated on him and betrayed his trust was more of a certainty than any suspicions she had about him and Monique. Hadn't he told her, time and again, that the beautiful actress meant nothing to him? If she loved him, why hadn't she believed him?

She could understand why she had felt as she had at first; she had been so convinced of her hatred for Jason that she had wanted to pay him back for the way he had treated her the night they had met. And Andy had been her tool; despite her claim that she hadn't thought Jason would care about him, she had to admit that she had taken a perverse satisfaction in depriving him of his son. And to make matters worse, he now knew, or would soon figure out, once he talked to Steven Douglas, that she had been trying to do it again. He'd never forgive her—not twice. She had ruined any chance she had ever had for happiness. How could she have been so stupid?

Her thoughts on this subject were brought to an abrupt halt when the door flew open and Jason walked into the room. He closed the door silently behind him and the cold detachment of his movements was more frightening to Linda than his raging anger had ever been. She backed away as he came closer.

"I believe this is yours." He flung the sable coat on the bed.

Linda barely glanced at the fur. "How did you find me? What are you doing here? What do you want?"

Jason looked more disheveled than she had ever seen him. His usually neat hair was unkempt, as if he had been running his fingers through it. He wore no tie and his ruffled silk shirt was open at the collar. There was a menacing chill in his eyes as he placed his hands on her shoulders. "It seems we've been through this before, down in Laguna Beach. You were in a pink cottage then, too." He glanced around the room. "Although the similarity ends with the color."

"If you don't leave I'll call the desk."

Jason threw back his head and laughed. "Go ahead, call the desk; you'll only make a fool of yourself. The desk clerk is the one who told me where you were. He was unsure of your identity and called the house to confirm it. Kim drove me here, then returned home." His hands left her shoulders and he tossed his jacket onto the chair, following it with his creased evening shirt. "Now maybe everyone can get some rest." The muscles on his bare chest rippled as he sat on the bed and began taking off his shoes. "Since I've answered your questions, suppose you explain your relationship with Steve Douglas to me."

"I can't," Linda said, turning away from his probing eyes. "You'll never believe me."

"Try me."

Tonelessly Linda recited the events leading up to her employment.

"So you still want to take Andrew away from me?" Jason's voice had turned cruel again. "Nothing has changed. You can't stop punishing me for taking your precious virginity. You still have to even the score by taking away my son.

"No, not now," Linda said, turning to face him and shaking her head in denial. "I know you love him as much as I do. I'll give you custody. You can do so much more for him than I can. I won't fight you, but I would appreciate seeing him now and then. He doesn't have to know who I am." Her voice broke and she hid her face in her hands.

"Hush, don't cry." Jason's strong fingers lifted her chin and gently brushed the tears from her lashes. "You'll see him every day. You're not going anywhere. This is the second time you've thrown my life into a turmoil by disappearing, and I don't intend to let it happen again."

"Why, Jason? I said I wouldn't try to take Andy away from you. There's no need to stay married to me anymore."

"No need to stay married to you?" Jason groaned. "You

may as well say there's no need to breathe the air. I love you so much I can't bear to be apart from you, and I'm willing to wait forever, if that's how long it takes to make you forgive me for hurting you the way I did. I want you to love me. I need you so much."

"You love me?" Linda's voice was barely audible.

"Of course I love you. I think I loved you from the very first moment I set eyes on you at that ridiculous studio party. That was why I was so angry later in the evening. You had affected me the way no other woman ever had. I usually have pretty good control over my emotions, and I didn't like to think I could forget everything in the arms of an innocent young thing from Kansas. I shouldn't have taken advantage of you, but I wanted you so much I couldn't stop myself. I just kept going until it was too late to turn back. I hated myself for what I had done. I was so angry that I wanted to lash out at someone; that's why I screamed at you. But when I woke up the next morning all I wanted was to hold you in my arms and make love to you again; I couldn't get enough of you. When you weren't there I nearly went insane; I knew I had to find you. At first I told myself that I just wanted to apologize. Then the thought of you lying in someone else's arms began driving me wild. I knew I couldn't go on without you."

"You didn't marry me just because of Andy?"

"When I first started looking for you I had no notion of Andrew's birth. If you recall, you did a very successful job of keeping that knowledge from me. It was you I needed, you I set out to find. I haven't wanted any other woman since that night we met a year and a half ago. You've enchanted me and made all other women undesirable by comparison."

Linda raised her hands, curling her fingers around his tautly muscled neck. "Oh, Jason, I loved you from that first moment I saw you. I thought you loved me, too. Then, when you screamed at me, I was so ashamed of my love that I didn't think I could ever face you again. I only went to work for Karizma Records because it was a chance to make something of myself. I had to prove that I was capable of supporting myself and Andy. I couldn't bear to have you treat me like some naïve simpleton."

"Well, you've made your point. As the chairman of the Board of JMR Industries, which now includes Karizma Records, let me state that I intend to hold you to your recording contract. Your voice is too good to be wasted in tiny out-of-the-way coffeehouses. Andy and his future sisters and brothers will just have to adjust to the fact that their mother is a famous recording star. I know they'll be just as proud of you as I am."

"Andy?" Linda said.

"Maybe I was being too formal before." Jason grinned. "And as you said, I can't always have my own way. Not with a lady as determined as you are."

Linda smiled and stroked her hands across his cheeks, trying to smooth the tension lines in his face. "You don't mind if I sing with the Sapphires?"

Jason shook his head. "I would never stop talent from being known."

"And Monique? I mean tonight . . . you and she . . . ?"

"She was so excited about her Oscar that I didn't have the heart to push her away. But we had a talk after you left, not long, but to the point, and I think she understands that I'm incapable of loving any woman but you."

"That night, after we made love, when you yelled at me . . . I was so frightened . . . so hurt."

He put his arms around her and held her closer. "I know that now. If I could just take back those words . . . But I had always been so in control of myself, until you. . . . I hated my own weakness."

Linda sighed. He had been just as helpless that night as she had been. Neither of them had been able to check their racing emotions. "Oh, Jason, we've been such fools."

"No more, my darling, everything is under control now. As I started to say, as the head of JMR Industries, I'm going to enforce your singing contract."

He smiled and his fingers moved lower, caressing the bare flesh of her back. "And, as your devoted husband, let me further state that I expect you to honor every aspect of our marriage contract. And that goes into effect immediately—I can't wait any longer. I'm starved for the touch of you." His hand tugged at the zipper of her gown and slipped it off her shoulders until it fell in a heap around her feet.

"Let me tell you about this hotel," he said, lifting her into his arms. "It's a favorite trysting spot of Hollywood stars. No one will ever disturb you and the help only comes to bring you necessities, like food, if you call for them. It's the perfect spot for the honeymoon we never had. I keep this cottage for visiting V.I.P.'s, but I have a feeling that you and I may get more use out of it than anyone else."

Linda's eyes met his as he lowered her to the bed and began running his fingers through her hair, removing the pins that had confined her tresses and fanning them out on the silken pillow like a golden halo of love. He switched off the lamp and covered her body with his.

Her arms circled his neck, urging him closer. As his kiss hardened against her lips and his body aroused desires hidden deep within her she knew that he would always be the master of her dreams . . . her life . . . her love.

6 brand new Silhouette Special Editions yours for 15 days–Free!

For the reader who wants more...more story...more detail and description...more realism...and more romance...in paperback originals, 1/3 longer than our regular Silhouette Romances. Love lingers longer in new Silhouette Special Editions. Love weaves an intricate, provocative path in a third more pages than you have just enjoyed. It is love as you have always wanted it to be—and more —intriguingly depicted by your favorite Silhouette authors in the inimitable Silhouette style.

15-Day Free Trial Offer

We will send you 6 new Silhouette Special Editions to keep for 15 days absolutely free! If you decide not to keep them, send them back to us, you pay nothing. But if you enjoy them as much as we think you will, keep them and pay the invoice enclosed with your trial shipment. You will then automatically become a member of the Special Edition Book Club and receive 6 more romances every month. There is no minimum number of books to buy and you can cancel at any time.

IT'S YOUR OWN SPECIAL TIME

Contemporary romances for today's women.
Each month, six very special love stories will be yours
from SILHOUETTE. Look for them wherever books are sold
or order now from the coupon below.

$1.50 each

Hampson	☐ 1 ☐ 4 ☐ 16 ☐ 27 ☐ 28 ☐ 52 ☐ 94	Browning	☐ 12 ☐ 38 ☐ 53 ☐ 73 ☐ 93
Stanford	☐ 6 ☐ 25 ☐ 35 ☐ 46 ☐ 58 ☐ 88	Michaels	☐ 15 ☐ 32 ☐ 61 ☐ 87
		John	☐ 17 ☐ 34 ☐ 57 ☐ 85
Hastings	☐ 13 ☐ 26	Beckman	☐ 8 ☐ 37 ☐ 54 ☐ 96
Vitek	☐ 33 ☐ 47 ☐ 84	Wisdom	☐ 49 ☐ 95
Wildman	☐ 29 ☐ 48	Halston	☐ 62 ☐ 83

☐ 5 Goforth	☐ 22 Stephens	☐ 50 Scott	☐ 81 Roberts
☐ 7 Lewis	☐ 23 Edwards	☐ 55 Ladame	☐ 82 Dailey
☐ 9 Wilson	☐ 24 Healy	☐ 56 Trent	☐ 86 Adams
☐ 10 Caine	☐ 30 Dixon	☐ 59 Vernon	☐ 89 James
☐ 11 Vernon	☐ 31 Halldorson	☐ 60 Hill	☐ 90 Major
☐ 14 Oliver	☐ 36 McKay	☐ 63 Brent	☐ 92 McKay
☐ 19 Thornton	☐ 39 Sinclair	☐ 71 Ripy	☐ 97 Clay
☐ 20 Fulford	☐ 43 Robb	☐ 76 Hardy	☐ 98 St. George
☐ 21 Richards	☐ 45 Carroll	☐ 78 Oliver	☐ 99 Camp

$1.75 each

Stanford	☐ 100 ☐ 112 ☐ 131	Hampson	☐ 108 ☐ 119 ☐ 128 ☐ 136 ☐ 147 ☐ 151 ☐ 155
Hardy	☐ 101 ☐ 130		
Cork	☐ 103 ☐ 148	Browning	☐ 113 ☐ 142
Vitek	☐ 104 ☐ 139 ☐ 157	Michaels	☐ 114 ☐ 146
Dailey	☐ 106 ☐ 118 ☐ 153	Beckman	☐ 124 ☐ 154
Bright	☐ 107 ☐ 125	Roberts	☐ 127 ☐ 143

Coming next month from
Silhouette Romances

Logic Of The Heart by Dixie Browning

Emma was looking forward to seeing the romantic island of Hatteras, and meeting Dan Slater added to the magic. She could see herself slipping into his arms and falling under his spell. . . .

Devil's Bargain by Elaine Camp

Was Alexis being caught up in an evil scheme or was Drayce's renewed love for her genuine? Their once passionate marriage seemed too distant to recapture those lost moments of ecstasy. Yet suddenly Drayce made Alexis forget why escape was so important!

Flight To Romance by Tracy Sinclair

Jennifer was not going to refuse Kalim Al Kahira, when he asked her to return with him to Egypt. She told herself her career demanded that she go—until she realized that there was no way to refuse his dark, penetrating eyes.

In Name Only by Roxanne Jarrett

Jill traveled to Brazil to enter into an arranged marriage. She was determined not to be ruled by her new husband, but soon she found herself unable to deny the mad passions that filled her with desire.

Sweet Surrender by Donna Vitek

Suzanne's trip to Italy turned out to be anything but the quiet visit she anticipated. For once she met Jared Caine she felt compelled to compete for his attention and show him the depth and breadth of her love.

The Second Time by Janet Dailey

Dawn returned home to the Florida Keys to seek peace in the turquoise waters. But soon calm waters are turned into turbulent seas when passions are ignited by her old flame Slater MacBride.